00 JAN 1999

;6

CHECKED — JUL 2008

SOLIHULL
CEC   LIBRARY
RECEIVED   26.4.94
STOCK
NO.   53186
CLASS
NO.
LB:
9J 2

D0230727

CHECKED   JUL 2008

CHECKED - JAN 2003

THE BRITISH ISLES

SECOND EDITION

SOLIHULL S.F.C. LIBRARY

DAVID WAUGH

Nelson

Thomas Nelson and Sons Ltd
Nelson House Mayfield Road
Walton-on-Thames Surrey
KT12 5PL UK

51 York Place
Edinburgh
EH1 3JD UK

Thomas Nelson (Hong Kong) Ltd
Toppan Building 10/F
22A Westlands Road
Quarry Bay Hong Kong

Thomas Nelson Australia
102 Dodds Street
South Melbourne
Victoria 3205 Australia

Nelson Canada
1120 Birchmount Road
Scarborough Ontario
M1K 5G4 Canada

© David Waugh 1983, 1990
First published by Thomas Nelson and Sons Ltd
1983
Second edition 1990

ISBN 0-17-434299-3

NPN 9 8 7 6 5 4 3

All rights reserved. No paragraph of this
publication may be reproduced, copied or
transmitted save with written permission or in
accordance with the provisions of the Copyright,
Design and Patents Act 1988, or under the terms
of any licence permitting limited copying issued
by the Copyright Licensing Agency, 90
Tottenham Court Road, London W1P 9HE.

Any person who does any unauthorised act in
relation to this publication may be liable to
criminal prosecution and civil claims for damages.

Printed and bound in Hong Kong

The publishers are grateful to the following for
permission to reproduce photographs and
copyright material:

Ace photo: p.92 fig 11.7, p.121 fig 15.7; Aerofilms:
p.56 fig 7.24; Airviews: p.113 fig. 13.10; Asda: p.96
fig 11.14 and 11.15; Associated Press: p.41 fig 6.9;
Barnabys Picture Library: p.117 fig 14.5; Biofotos/
Heather Angel: p.11 fig 1.20; British Railway Board:
p.84 fig 10.18, p.89 fig 10.32; British Coal: p.43 fig
14.6; J Allan Cash: p.8 fig 1.14, p.16 fig 2.18, p.17
fig 2.21 p.26 fig 3.19, p.83 fig 10.14, p.92 fig 11.8,
p.100 fig 12.15, p.113 fig 13.12; Celtic Picture
Library: p.60 fig 8.7; Central Studio, Carlisle p.15
fig 2.13; John Urling-Clark: p.66 fig 8.23, p.80 fig
10.7, p.91 fig 11.4, p.91 fig 11.5; Department of
the Environment: p.127 fig 16.2; Delta Office Park:
p.54 fig 7.21; Forestry Commission: p.28 fig 4.3,
4.15, 4.16; Eldon Square City Council: p.93 fig
11.9; Greg Evans: p.87 fig 10.28; University of
Belfast: p.77 fig 9.16; G.S.F. Picture Library: p.66
fig 8.24: Sally and Richard Greenhill: p.90 fig 11.3:
Glasgow City Council: p.60 fig 8.8; Greenpeace:
p.126 fig 16.1(3 pics); Robert Harding Picture
Library: p.81 fig 10.11, p.118 fig 14.8; Holt Studios:
p.18 fig 3.1 (2 pics); Hunting Aerofilms: p.7 fig 1.9,
p.10 fig 1.15, p.11 fig 1.17, p.17 fig 2.23; Colour
Library International: p.105 fig 12.16 and 12.17;
Northumberland Water Authority: p.36 fig 5.6;
Oxford Scientific Films: p.11 fig 1.21, p.27 fig 3.20,
p.27 fig 3.21, p.31 fig 4.11; Pictor International:
p.46 fig 6.22, p.52 fig 7.14; Picturepoint: p.19 fig
3.5, p.26 fig 3.18, p.24 fig 3.14, p.44 fig 6.17, p.44
fig 6.20, p.107 fig 12.12; Popperfoto: p.14 fig 2.10;
Reed Farming: p.18 fig 3.2; Chris Ridgers
Photography: p.52 fig 7.14, p.63 fig 8.17; Science
Photo Library: p.46 fig 6.23, p.47 fig 6.25; p.54 fig
7.20; Sealand Aerial Photography: p.55 fig 7.22;
Scottish Development Agency: p.125 fig 15.15 and
15.16; Severn Trent Water Authority: p.34 fig 5.2;
Sky scan: p.17 fig 2.20; Spectrum Colour Library:
p.52 fig 7.14, p.20 fig 3.8, p.28 fig 4.2, p.86 fig
10.23, p.121 fig 15.4 and 15.6; Telegraph Colour
Library: p.73 fig 9.8, p.80 fig 10.6, p.83 fig 10.16,
p.108 fig 13.1, p.126 fig 16.1; United Kingdom
Atomic Energy Authority: p.44 fig 6.17; Nelsons:
p.81 fig 10.10; David Waugh: p.7 fig 1.8; p.51
fig 7.13, p.20 fig 3.7, p.61 fig 8.10 and 8.11, p.63
fig 8.14, p.63 fig 8.15, p.63 fig 8.16, p.64 fig
8.18, p.65 fig 8.19, 8.20 and 8.21, p.66 fig 8.22;
Jonathan Waugh: p.15 fig 2.16, p.60 fig 8.6 and
8.8.

CONTENTS

● THE DRAINAGE BASIN

This is an area of land drained by a main river and its tributaries (Figure 1.1). Its boundary, marked by a ridge of higher land, is called a watershed. The drainage basin forms an 'open system' and is part of the larger 'closed system' of the hydrological cycle (Figure 5.1).

It is an open system because it has:

1 inputs, where water enters the system though precipitation, and

2 outputs, where water is lost to the system, either by the river carrying water to the sea or by evapotranspiration. Evapotranspiration is the loss of moisture directly from rivers or lakes (evaporation) or from vegetation (transpiration).

Within the system some of the water will be stored within lakes or the soil while the remainder will pass through it by a series of transfers (e.g. infiltration, throughflow and surface run-off). A typical British drainage basin system is shown in Figure 1.2.

When it begins to rain, most of the water droplets will be intercepted by trees and plants. Interception is greatest in summer. If the rain falls as a short, light shower then little water will reach the ground and it may be lost immediately to the system by evaporation. When the rain is heavier and lasts longer, the water, once it has made the surface damp and soft, will begin to infiltrate. Infiltration is the downward movement of water through tiny pores in the soil. It will be greatest in a porous rock or soil such as chalk or sand, as this contains many pore spaces, and least in an impermeable rock or soil such as granite or clay. The water will then either be stored in the soil or slowly transferred. If the movement of water is

sideways, a process called throughflow, it may eventually form a spring on a valley side. If the movement is downwards, a process known as percolation, it will form groundwater and will be stored at a considerable depth.

Surface run-off, also known as overland flow, occurs if:

■ the storm is too heavy for the water to infiltrate into the soil,

■ the soil is impermeable,

■ the soil is saturated i.e. the pores have been, filled with water from earlier storms. The level of saturation (Figure 1.2), which varies seasonally, is known as the water-table.

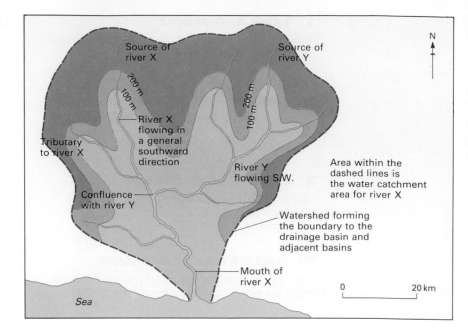

Figure 1.1 The drainage basin of a river

Figure 1.2 The drainage basin system

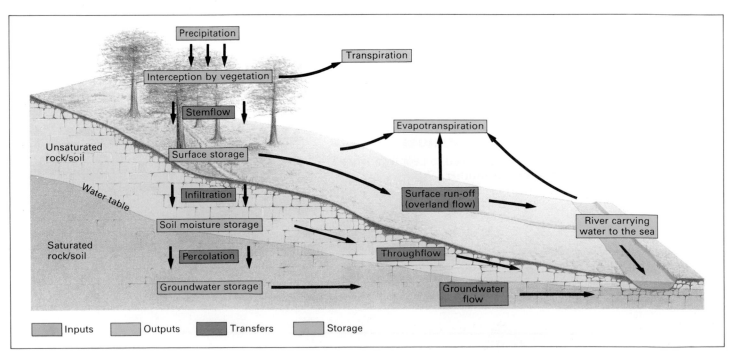

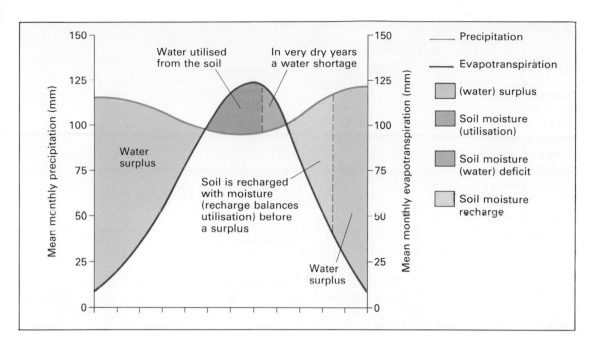

Figure 1.3 The water balance

The water balance

This is the balance between the inputs and outputs in the system. It can be expressed as a formula:

Precipitation = Run-off + Evapotranspiration
  (input)   (outputs)

In Britain most precipitation usually falls in winter when temperatures, and therefore evapotranspiration, are lowest. This causes large amounts of moisture to be stored in the soil and gives high river levels. As rainfall tends to decrease in summer and as temperatures rise, river levels fall. Vegetation, now growing rapidly, has to use moisture stored within the soil (Figure 1.3). If there is a drought, as happened in 1976 and 1989, then the reserve of soil moisture will be utilised. Should a soil moisture deficiency occur then plants will begin to die. In autumn, as rainfall increases, temperatures decrease and vegetation stops growing, the soil will become recharged with moisture until, eventually, there is a water surplus.

In a normal year (Figure 1.3) most of Britain, except for some places in the South-east, will have a surplus water balance.

Velocity and discharge

Velocity is the speed of the river. It is measured in metres per second.

Volume is the amount of water in the river. It is the cross sectional area of the river's channel measured in square metres.

Discharge is the velocity of the river times its volume given in cumecs. A cumec is the number of cubic metres per second passing a given point.

Flow regimes

This term is used to describe seasonal variations in the volume of a river. The average regime results

mainly from the climate within the drainage basin. e.g. the amount and distribution of rainfall. Figure 1.4 shows monthly precipitation and run-off totals at a recording station in the basin of the River Swale in North Yorkshire. Run-off is the amount of precipitation which eventually reaches the river and is not stored in the basin nor lost through evapotransporation.

Why do British rivers have a greater discharge in winter than summer?

- Rainfall amounts are higher (time of most depressions).
- Ground may be frozen and acts as an impermeable rock.
- Low temperatures reduce evaporation from rivers and the soil.
- Plants are dormant, reducing transpiration.
- Trees shed their leaves which reduces interception and increases surface run-off.

(Discharge will decrease during times of heavy snowfall when water is held in storage until temperatures rise and the snow melts).

Figure 1.4 Rainfall and run-off for a river in the Pennines

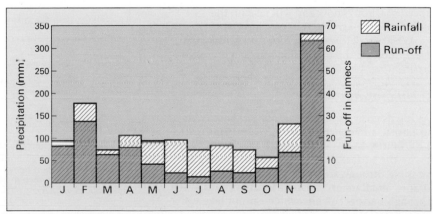

Why do some rivers have a greater discharge than others?

- The north and west of Britain have heavier rainfall.
- The south and east have, in summer, higher temperatures, more sunshine and, therefore, higher rates of evapotranspiration.
- Soil moisture cannot be stored in a drainage basin floored by impermeable rock as, unlike porous rock, water cannot infiltrate.
- Upland areas have thinner soils and a steeper relief (slopes).
- Forested areas will intercept more rain, have higher rates of transpiration and will utilise moisture from the soil.
- Rivers are often affected by human action, e.g. flood control and water extracted for industrial, farming and domestic purposes.

The storm hydrograph

This is a graph to illustrate the discharge of a river. It shows how river levels are affected by individual storms or longer periods of wet weather. When the storm begins (Figure 1.5) river levels do not begin to rise immediately as little moisture falls directly into the channel. The first water to reach the river will be surface run-off supplemented later by throughflow. The increase in discharge is shown by the rising limb. The gap between the time of peak (maximum) rainfall and peak discharge is called lag time.

A river with a short lag time and high discharge is more likely to flood. It will also, during dry periods, be likely to have very low levels.

Human activity affecting drainage basin systems

1 Afforestation

Initially the clearance and drainage of land in preparation for tree planting will increase run-off. However as the trees grow they will reduce the risk of flooding. Branches and leaves will increase interception, reducing run-off by up to 30%, and increase evapotranspiration. Roots will delay the speed of throughflow and will take up the moisture necessary for the trees survival.

Why will deforestation (the cutting down of trees) increase the risk of flooding in a drainage basin?

2 Urbanisation

As towns grow in size the amount of land covered in tarmac and concrete also increases. This reduces infiltration. Excess water, which might otherwise lie on the surface, is drained away as quickly as possible through an artificial system of gutters and drains. Small urban streams are often channelised through narrow culverts which cannot take water from heavy storms.

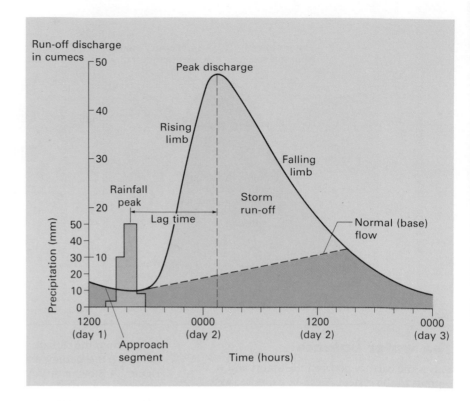

Figure 1.5 The storm (flood) hydrograph

● RIVER PROCESSES AND LANDFORMS

Energy is necessary in any system, not just the drainage basin, for transfers to take place. In the case of a river most of this energy, an estimated 95% under normal conditions, is needed to overcome friction. Most friction occurs at the wetted perimeter, i.e. where water comes into contact with the river's banks and bed, although air (wind) resistance can also be important. The channel of a mountain stream, often filled with boulders, creates much friction. As a result, water flows less quickly than in a lowland river where the channel is wider and deeper (Figure 1.6).

Following a period of heavy rain, or after the confluence with a major tributary, the volume of

Figure 1.6 Velocity and discharge in the upper and lower course of a Pennine stream

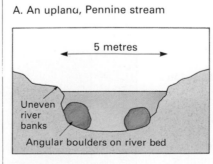
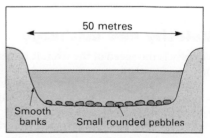

A. An upland, Pennine stream

B. A lowland river

5 metres

50 metres

Uneven river banks

Angular boulders on river bed

Smooth banks

Small rounded pebbles

Despite waterfalls where the velocity is locally high, the large number of angular boulders and uneven banks give a large wetted perimeter which increases friction and reduces velocity

Here there is a relatively smaller wetted perimeter in comparison to the volume. Due to this, and the smooth banks and bedload, friction is reduced allowing velocity to increase

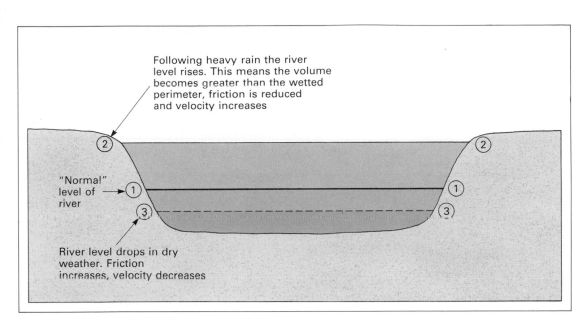

Figure 1.7 Changes in river velocity due to changes in discharge

Following heavy rain the river level rises. This means the volume becomes greater than the wetted perimeter, friction is reduced and velocity increases

"Normal" level of river

River level drops in dry weather. Friction increases, velocity decreases

the river will increase. As less water will be in contact with the wetted perimeter then friction will be reduced and the river will increase its velocity (Figure 1.7). The surplus energy, resulting from the decrease in friction, can now be used to pick up and transport material. The greater the velocity of a river the greater the amount of material, in both quantity and size, that can be carried. The transported material is known as the load of the river. There are three main processes of transportation:

1 in solution where material is dissolved before being moved,

2 in suspension when fine material, e.g. clay and silt, is held up and carried by the rivers movement,

3 by saltation and traction where the larger material, forming the bed-load, is bounced and rolled along.

When the load comes into contact with the bed and banks it can cause erosion i.e. the wearing away of the land. A river may erode by one of four processes:

1 corrosion is when the banks and bed are dissolved,

2 corrasion results from material being rubbed against the banks and bed,

3 attrition is when bed-load collides and the boulders break,

4 hydraulic action is caused by the sheer force of the water.

Several landforms resulting from erosion are shown in Figure 1.8.

Following a dry period the discharge and velocity of a river will decrease and its load, beginning with the heaviest, will be deposited. Deposition also produces a number of landforms (Figure 1.9).

Figure 1.8 Landforms in the upper course of a Pennine stream (left)

Figure 1.9 Landforms in the lower course of a river (right)

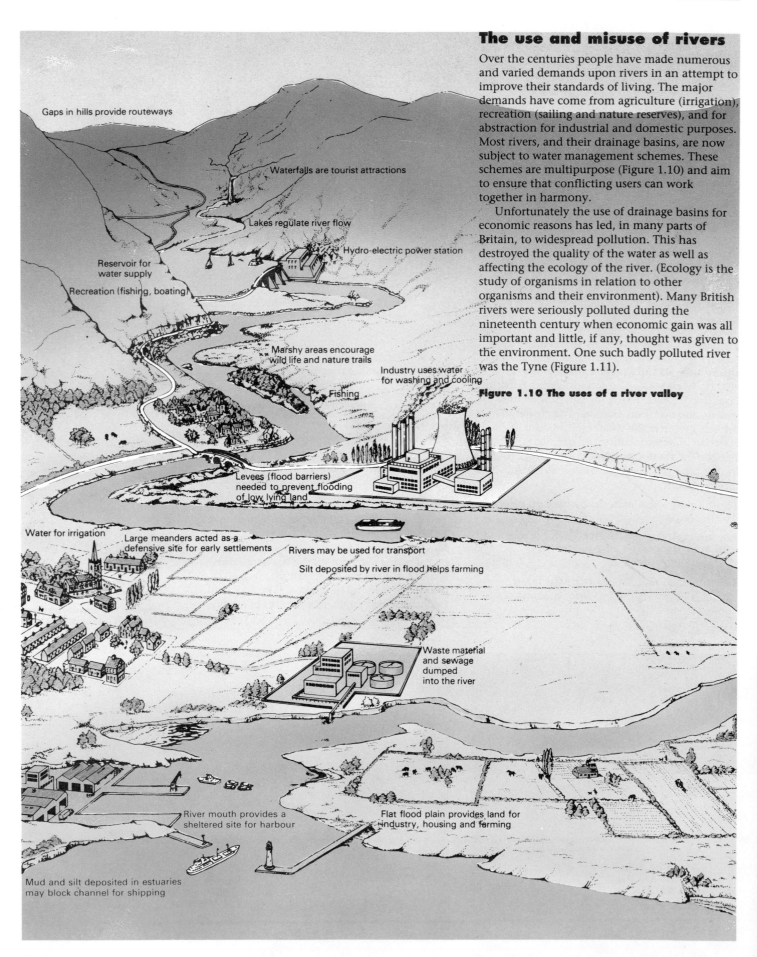

Gaps in hills provide routeways

Waterfalls are tourist attractions

Lakes regulate river flow

Hydro-electric power station

Reservoir for water supply

Recreation (fishing, boating)

Marshy areas encourage wild life and nature trails

Industry uses water for washing and cooling

Fishing

Levees (flood barriers) needed to prevent flooding of low lying land

Water for irrigation

Large meanders acted as a defensive site for early settlements

Rivers may be used for transport

Silt deposited by river in flood helps farming

Waste material and sewage dumped into the river

River mouth provides a sheltered site for harbour

Flat flood plain provides land for industry, housing and farming

Mud and silt deposited in estuaries may block channel for shipping

The use and misuse of rivers

Over the centuries people have made numerous and varied demands upon rivers in an attempt to improve their standards of living. The major demands have come from agriculture (irrigation), recreation (sailing and nature reserves), and for abstraction for industrial and domestic purposes. Most rivers, and their drainage basins, are now subject to water management schemes. These schemes are multipurpose (Figure 1.10) and aim to ensure that conflicting users can work together in harmony.

Unfortunately the use of drainage basins for economic reasons has led, in many parts of Britain, to widespread pollution. This has destroyed the quality of the water as well as affecting the ecology of the river. (Ecology is the study of organisms in relation to other organisms and their environment). Many British rivers were seriously polluted during the nineteenth century when economic gain was all important and little, if any, thought was given to the environment. One such badly polluted river was the Tyne (Figure 1.11).

Figure 1.10 The uses of a river valley

By the mid-1950s many rivers, including the Thames, Mersey and Clyde, were 'dead', and salmon, a pointer to the quality of the water, were no longer seen. Rivers not only gave off obnoxious smells, they were a source of disease. There were tales of people who, although saved from drowning after falling into rivers, later died from the effects of swallowing the dirty water. The responsibility for cleaning up rivers lies, in England and Wales, with the ten Water Authorities (Figure 5.4). In 1974 the Northumbrian Water Authority began to clean upon the River Tyne — the then largest single improvement scheme in Britain. Its aims were to:

- clean up the 32 km of the Tyne nearest to its mouth (as well as 14 km of beaches to either side of its mouth),
- construct sewage treatment works along both banks so that no untreated sewage would be discharged into the river after 1990,
- lay 75 km of new sewers so that flood water from heavy rainfall would be kept separate from domestic sewage,
- prevent industrial waste and domestic refuse being deposited in the river.

By 1988 (Figure 1.12):
- over 80% of untreated sewage had been diverted from the river,
- with less pollution there had been an increase in the oxygen content of the water and a return of the salmon,
- the river no longer gave off odious smells.

However a report on the state of Britain's rivers in February 1989 claimed that they were being polluted at a faster rate than at any time since national records had begun. It was estimated that 725 km of top-quality river had been polluted in the previous two years. After years of progress in controlling pollution, rivers in England, Wales and, to a lesser extent, Scotland were being poisoned by waste. Of 23 000 reported cases of river pollution in 1988:

- 37% were caused by industry (mainly those connected with oil, chemicals and mining),
- 20% were the result of the Water Authorities themselves releasing untreated sewage,
- 19%, and a growing proportion, was blamed upon farmers (Chapter 3),
- 24% were unexplained.

A major present environmental issue is 'Who will be responsible, and who will pay, for future clean up schemes following the privatisation of water?'

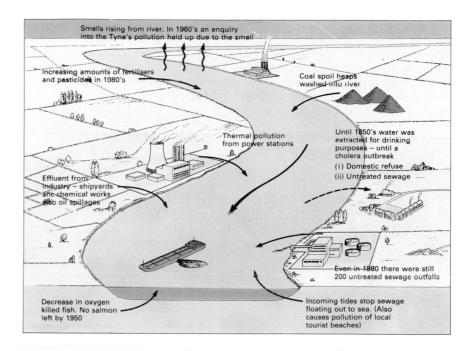

Figure 1.11 Pollution of the River Tyne

Labels in figure:
- Smells rising from river. In 1960's an enquiry into the Tyne's pollution held up due to the smell
- Increasing amounts of fertilisers and pesticides in 1980's
- Coal spoil heaps washed into river
- Thermal pollution from power stations
- Until 1850's water was extracted for drinking purposes — until a cholera outbreak (i) Domestic refuse (ii) Untreated sewage
- Effluent from industry — shipyards and chemical works also oil spillages
- Even in 1980 there were still 200 untreated sewage outfalls
- Decrease in oxygen killed fish. No salmon left by 1950
- Incoming tides stop sewage floating out to sea. (Also causes pollution of local tourist beaches)

Figure 1.12 The 'clean up' of the River Tyne

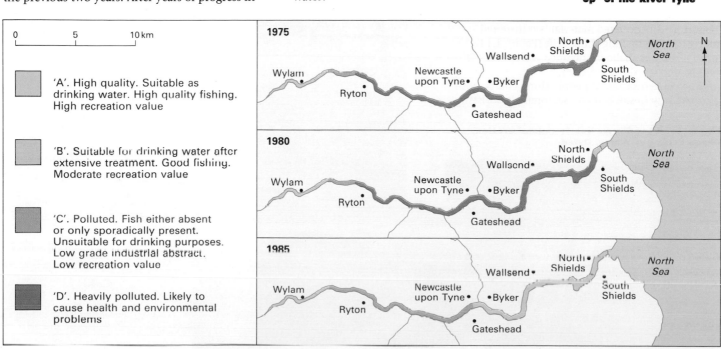

Key:
- 'A'. High quality. Suitable as drinking water. High quality fishing. High recreation value
- 'B'. Suitable for drinking water after extensive treatment. Good fishing. Moderate recreation value
- 'C'. Polluted. Fish either absent or only sporadically present. Unsuitable for drinking purposes. Low grade industrial abstract. Low recreation value
- 'D'. Heavily polluted. Likely to cause health and environmental problems

Maps labelled 1975, 1980, 1985 showing Wylam, Ryton, Newcastle upon Tyne, Byker, Gateshead, Wallsend, North Shields, South Shields, North Sea.

Scale: 0 5 10 km

COASTS

Waves are created by the transfer of energy from winds blowing over the surface of the sea. The largest waves are produced when winds are strong, blow for lengthy periods and cross large tracts of ocean. The maximum distance of water over

has led to conflict between different types of users as well as between people and nature (Figure 1.16). Coastal management is essential if coastal resources are to be used sensibly with minimal interference with nature. In most cases there are a range of options rather than one single solution as to how coasts should be used.

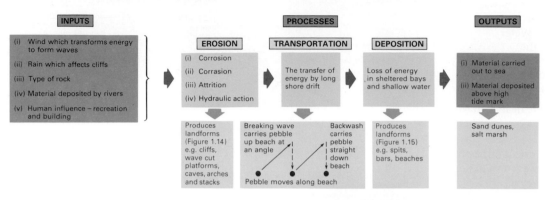

Figure 1.13 The coastal system

Figure 1.16 The uses and misuses of coasts

which winds can blow is called the fetch. In the case of Land's End the fetch is the south-west. As a wave reaches shallow water when it approaches land, its base will reduce speed due to friction with the sea-bed. The top of the wave, unaffected by friction, becomes higher and steeper until it breaks. There are two types of wave:

1 Constructive waves are when most of the energy is used in the swash to carry material up the beach.

2 Destructive waves are when most of the energy is concentrated in the backwash. This results in material being moved down the beach.

Waves, like rivers (page 7), can erode by one of four processes:corrosion, corrasion, solution and hydraulic action (Figure 1.13). Erosion can 1 undercut and cause the retreat of cliffs to form wave cut platforms and 2 widen joints and areas of weakness to form caves, arches and stacks (Figure 1.14). Loosened material is transferred along beaches by long shore drift (Figure 1.13) until it reaches shallow, sheltered water where it will be deposited (Figure 1.15).

The concentration of people along coasts, both permanently (residents) and seasonally (tourists),

Figure 1.14 Landforms due to coastal erosion, Green Bridge of Wales, Dyfed

Figure 1.15 Landforms due to coastal deposition

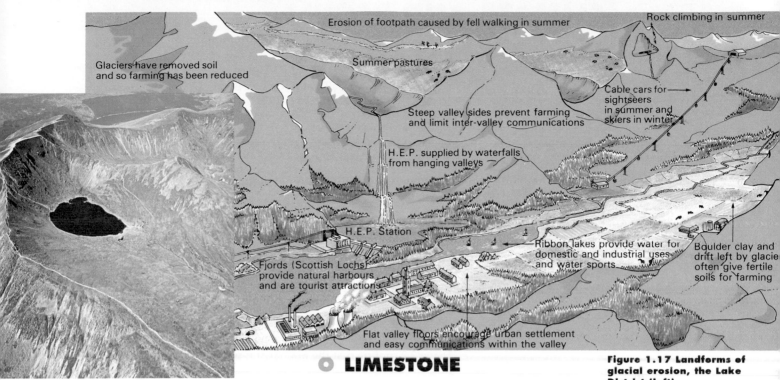

Erosion of footpath caused by fell walking in summer

Rock climbing in summer

Glaciers have removed soil and so farming has been reduced

Summer pastures

Steep valley sides prevent farming and limit inter-valley communications

Cable cars for sightseers in summer and skiers in winter

H.E.P. supplied by waterfalls from hanging valleys

H.E.P. Station

Fjords (Scottish Lochs) provide natural harbours and are tourist attractions

Ribbon lakes provide water for domestic and industrial uses and water sports

Boulder clay and drift left by glacier often give fertile soils for farming

Flat valley floors encourage urban settlement and easy communications within the valley

Figure 1.17 Landforms of glacial erosion, the Lake District (left)

Figure 1.18 Uses of a glaciated valley (right)

○ GLACIAL

It is the changes in the inputs into the system which are responsible for different landscapes. In the case of glaciation a fall in temperature causes snow to fall and ice to form. As this accumulates in the mountains it, together with loose rock called moraine, is transferred downhill, under gravity, as a glacier. As temperatures rise the ice begins to melt (ablation) giving outputs of meltwater and evaporation. Ice erodes and transports material differently to water and consequently produces different landforms to those of a river (Figure 1.17). Glaciated areas are used, like river valleys and coasts, for human activity. Similarly this may lead to conflicts between nature and various land-users (Figure 1.18).

Attempt to produce a systems diagram, similar to Figure 1.13, for a glaciated valley.

○ LIMESTONE

Limestone is composed of calcium carbonate and forms its own distinctive scenery (sometimes referred to as karst). This is because:

■ Limestone is a sedimentary rock which has been laid down in layers. The horizontal junctions between layers are called bedding planes, and the vertical lines of weakness are known as joints (Figure 1.19).

■ Calcium carbonate is soluble in rainwater. As the water dissolves the limestone, especially along bedding planes and down joints, a variety of features are formed. These are illustrated in Figures 1.19, 1.20 and 1.21.

■ Rivers tend to follow lines of weakness and to flow underground dissolving the rock to form large caves or to deposit the dissolved limestone in the form of stalactites, stalagmites and pillars (Figure 1.21). This leaves the surface of the limestone area dry.

Figure 1.20 Limestone pavement with clints and grykes, Malham, Yorkshire

Figure 1.21 A limestone dry valley, Malham Cove, Yorkshire

Figure 1.19 Landforms and land use in limestone areas

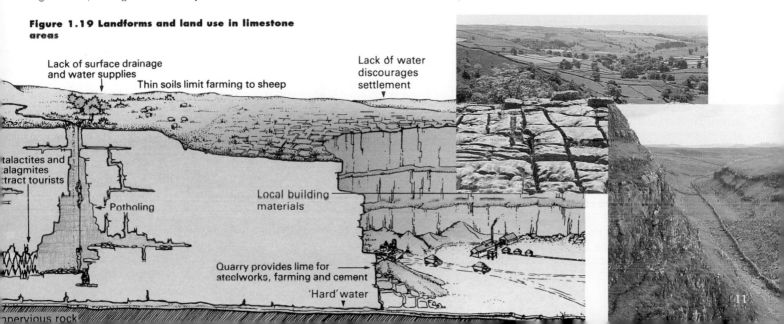

Lack of surface drainage and water supplies

Thin soils limit farming to sheep

Lack of water discourages settlement

talactites and alagmites tract tourists

Potholing

Local building materials

Quarry provides lime for steelworks, farming and cement

'Hard' water

npervious rock

Britain has:

- A variable climate, which means that the weather changes from day to day, and this makes it difficult to forecast.

- An equable climate, which means that extremes of heat or cold, or of drought or prolonged rainfall are rarely experienced.

If we wish to generalise about Britain's weather, we can say it has cool summers, mild winters, and a steady reliable rainfall throughout the whole year.

○ PRECIPITATION

The annual distribution of rainfall

Farming

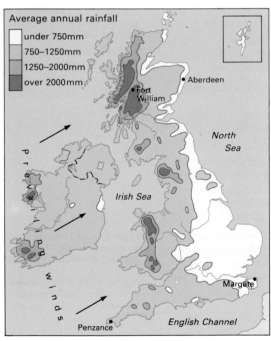

Figure 2.1 Average annual rainfall

The type of farming (arable or pastoral) in an area is determined by 'average' conditions, but extreme conditions (drought, heavy snowfall) can be a hazard to farming. Figure 2.1 shows the average annual rainfall for Britain. The West faces the Atlantic Ocean and receives south-westerly winds from the sea, often in the form of depressions which, together with the high mountains, cause heavy rainfall (in Figure 2.1, those areas over 1250 mm). Those areas, however, with over 750 mm tend to be too cloudy and wet for crops, but they give good pasture for cattle on the lowlands and sheep at higher levels. It is the drier South and East (with a rainfall of under 750 mm on Figure 2.1) that are best suited to crops — both fruit and cereals (Figure 3.6).

Water supply

As a result of the rainfall distribution in Britain (Figure 2.1) there is a water surplus in the North and West, and a water deficit in the South and East. Reservoirs have therefore to be built in such highland areas as Central Wales, the Lake District, and the Scottish Highlands, so that water can be stored there and then transferred to the more populated and industrial areas of lowland Britain (Figure. 5.5).

The reliability of rainfall

As in most parts of the world it is not how much rain falls but:

- at which time of year or season it occurs, and

- whether it comes in short, heavy downpours or as steady, gentle rain,

which is more important. The climate graphs in Figure 2.2 confirm that the west coast is wetter than the east and show that, although rain is fairly evenly spread throughout the year, most falls in autumn and winter.

Drought is relatively uncommon in Britain and so a long dry spell like the summers of 1976 and 1989 catches people unprepared (page 15). Reservoir levels fall (Figure 2.16) and the domestic supply is affected as well as farming and industry. Even in 'average' years, farmers need to use sprinklers in southern and eastern England (notice Margate, Figure 2.2).

Flooding results from periods of prolonged rain and can be serious in spring if this coincides with a time of snow-melt when the ground is still frozen. Yet the worst floods (page 14) often tend to follow summer thunderstorms when the hard ground cannot absorb the water and the resultant surface run-off (page 4) can disrupt transport, ruin crops and damage property (Figure 2.13).

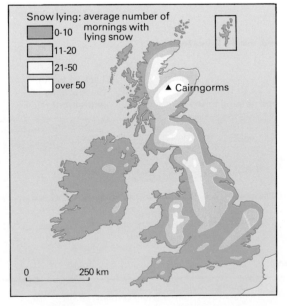

Figure 2.2 Climate graphs

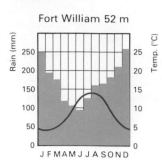

Fort William 52 m

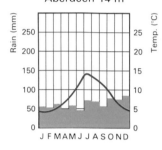

Aberdeen 14 m

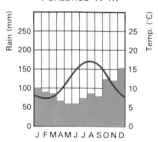

Penzance 17 m

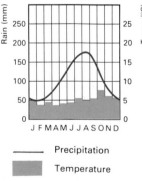

Margate 16 m

—— Precipitation

▨ Temperature

Figure 2.3 Duration of snow cover

⊙ TEMPERATURE

The length of the growing season can affect:

Farmers If they live in Cornwall or the Isles of Scilly (Figure 2.4) they can produce early flowers and vegetables long before the rest of Britain; but if they live in northern Britain, they find the summers too short for cereals to ripen.

Forestry workers Coniferous trees can survive in a much shorter growing season than deciduous trees and therefore the conifers are planted at higher altitudes and further north than their deciduous counterparts.

Summer temperatures

Figure 2.5 shows that the South is warmer than the North, and inland areas warmer than the coast. The result is that:

■ Farmers will grow fruit and cereals if they live in the South and East.

■ Tourists will prefer resorts along the South Coast. Figure 2.6 illustrates the fact that it is these southern parts which also get most hours of sunshine — indeed Margate advertises itself as Britain's 'Sunniest Resort'. But Britain rarely experiences long periods of sunbathing weather and hence large numbers go abroad for their holidays. If Britain does experience a hot spell, however, this often results in traffic congestion on major roads going to the coast; holiday makers packed on to beaches and the promenades; and the over-use of amenities.

■ A possible water shortage may occur. Figure 2.7 shows that the average annual evaporation rate is highest in the South-east of England. Indeed, summer evaporation exceeds summer precipitation and so there is a water shortage in both the soil and in reservoirs (Figure 1.3). Fortunately, in winter, with its lower temperatures and higher rainfall, there is a surplus which can refill the reservoirs and recharge the soil.

Figure 2.4 Length of the growing season

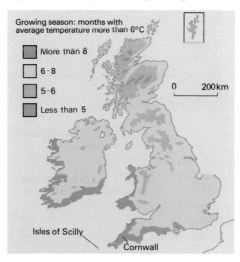

Figure 2.5 July temperatures

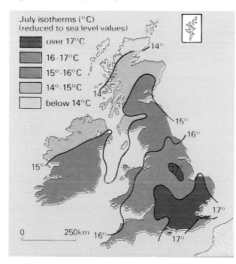

Figure 2.6 Hours of sunshine in July

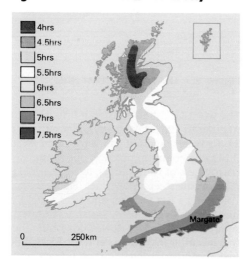

Winter temperatures

Figure 2.8 shows the pronounced warming effect of the North Atlantic Drift on the western shores of Britain. This warm current keeps ports ice-free and limits the duration of snow cover (Figure 2.3) compared with other parts of the world in latitudes the same as Britain. So it is only the Cairngorms and surrounding areas (Figure 2.3) that can provide winter sports. Yet when heavy snowfalls do occur, they tend to disrupt communications and, although relatively rare, can cause great hardship to upland farmers and their livestock (Figure 2.22).

Figure 2.7 Average annual evaporation

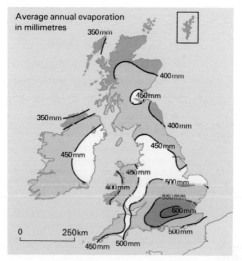

Figure 2.8 January temperatures

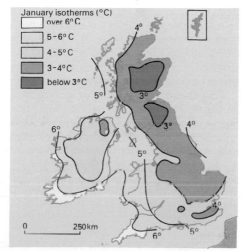

○ CLIMATIC HAZARDS

Too much rain

Landslides

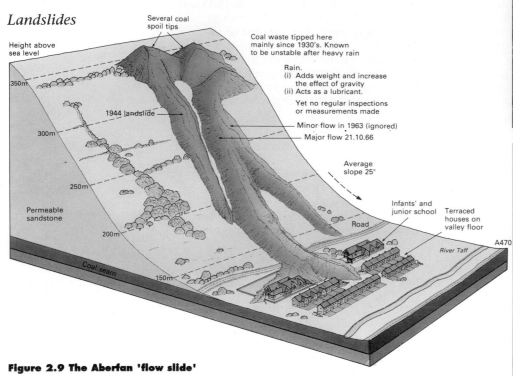

Figure 2.9 The Aberfan 'flow slide'

Labels in figure:
- Height above sea level
- 350m
- 300m
- 250m
- 200m
- 150m
- Permeable sandstone
- Coal seam
- 1944 landslide
- Several coal spoil tips
- Coal waste tipped here mainly since 1930's. Known to be unstable after heavy rain
- Rain.
  (i) Adds weight and increase the effect of gravity
  (ii) Acts as a lubricant.
- Yet no regular inspections or measurements made
- Minor flow in 1963 (ignored)
- Major flow 21.10.66
- Average slope 25°
- Infants' and junior school
- Road
- Terraced houses on valley floor
- River Taff
- A470

Figure 2.10 / 2.12 (right, Carlisle diagram) labels:
- Land left for grazing – limited potential flood damage
- Upstream radar used to monitor rainclo[ud] and rainfall
- Bedload extracted to deepen river and increase discharge
- River
- Golf cours[e]
- Made deeper, straightened, given flood ba[nks] and a concrete
- Land left for leisure (no buildings)
- Carli[sle] RFC
- Trinity school
- 2 metre high flood banks protect school,
- road and houses
- Carlisles' CBD ½ km
- R. Petteril
- A69 New[...]

The worst landslide disaster in Britain occurred at Aberfan in 1966. Like many other settlements in South Wales, Aberfan grew up around its colliery. It became common practice, due to the narrowness of valley floors, to tip the coal waste high on the steep valley sides (Figure 2.9). Following a wet October and after a night of heavy rain, tip number 7 became saturated and suddenly and rapidly flowed downhill. The time was just after 0900 hours and the local children had already assembled in their infants' and junior school. They were unaware of millions of tons of coal waste, rocks and sludge, followed by a second wave of liquid mud and sludge, rushing down the steep valley sides at a tremenduous pace. The flow, 15 metres deep, engulfed the school, a row of terraced houses and a farm. Of the 147 people who died, mainly due to suffocation, 116 were children. Almost a whole generation had been wiped out within seconds (Figure 2.10).

Less disastrous landslides occur frequently during times of excessive rainfall. Some of the most spectacular occur along Britain's south coast, especially in areas where softer rock overlies harder rock. As the softer rock becomes heavier, due to the weight of water, it can flow over the underlying rock. Such events may cause loss of property but, thankfully, rarely human or animal life.

Figure 2.11 Possible causes of flooding in Carlisle

River floods

Although there may only be one single factor as to why a river should overflow its banks, often a flood results from a combination of reasons. Floods may affect human activity (e.g. the Severn Valley in February 1990), but fortunately, in Britain, sufficient warning can usually be given to avoid the loss of life and, because of our relative wealth and level of technology, their effect can often by minimised. Figure 2.11 and 2.13 shows the contributary causes and the effects of a major flood in Carlisle, while Figure 2.12 shows the attempts which were made by the local Water Authority to try to avoid a repeat occurence.

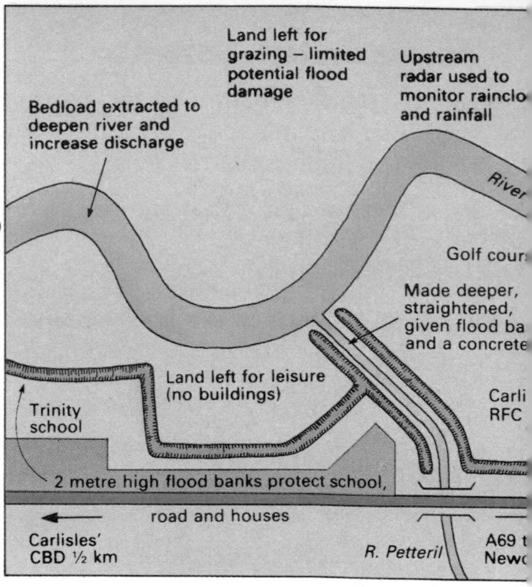

Figure 2.10 The town of Aberfan after the landslide

Figure 2.12 Attempted solutions to flooding in Carlisle

1 Causes of the flood

- 30 hours of heavy, prolonged rain caused by a stationary depression.
- Snow lying on the watershed (the Lake District) began to melt.
- The rocks in the upper drainage basin are impermeable.
- Previous cold weather had caused the ground in the upper drainage basin to freeze.
- The valley sides of the upper drainage basin are steep with very few trees growing on them.
- The ground nearer Carlisle was already saturated from earlier rain.
- Several new housing estates had increased the level of urbanisation.
- An exceptionally high spring tide prevented flood water escaping into the Solway Firth (the estuary at the mouth of the River Eden).
- A south-westerly gale caused a storm surge (page 16) at the river's mouth.

2 Effects of the flood

- 400 houses were flooded and 150 families had to be evacuated.
- Roads became impassable and police had either to rescue people or deliver food and candles by boat.
- Public services were disrupted with electricity and telephones cut off.
- Factories were flooded and some of their goods destroyed
- Farmers had to rescue their sheep and cattle.
- In some places soil was washed away, elsewhere silt killed grass.
- Drains overflowed causing unpleasant smells.

Figure 2.13 The effect of flooding, Carlisle

SOLIHULL S.F.C. LIBRARY

Too little rain — drought

Climatic conditions 1975-1976

During the summer of 1975, the depressions which bring cloud and rain from the Atlantic were diverted to the north of Britain. The result was a hot, dry summer which caused reservoirs and underground supplies of water to run low. The winter of 1975-76 remained mild and dry. Apart from a wet May in northern England the dry weather continued throughout the country until the last few days of August 1976. During June, July and August, all of England and Wales received over 30% more than their expected amounts of sunshine while some areas in the south and east received over 50% more. They also had less than 60% of their normal rainfall (Figure 2.14). Water already in the soil and reservoirs was lost due to the high rates of evaporation.

Consequences of the drought

- A ban on hosepipes for gardens and cars was imposed in some areas by June, and by August several parts of the country were affected by rationing. Parts of Devon could only obtain water through standpipes for two weeks in late August. (Figure 2.15)

- People were encouraged to use showers rather than baths, and even to share their bathwater. As soils became drier in southern England, the clay shrank and cracked causing buildings to be damaged as their foundations moved.

- Farmers were badly hit, as the grass turned brown and stopped growing, and crops wilted under the hot sun. Yields of all crops fell, while grass was insufficient for cattle.

- Some industries had to close for one or two days each week to save water.

- Recreation and sport were affected. Cricket pitches and bowling greens could not be watered, while the drop in the level of lakes and reservoirs curtailed water-based activities.

- In southern England, much of the heather growing on the heathlands died due to lack of moisture. As these areas, together with coniferous forests and moorlands in the north and west of Britain, became tinder dry, fires broke out and caused considerable damage.

- Two reservoirs which fell to their lowest levels since they had been built were Haweswater in Cumbria (Figure 2.16) and Derwent in North Derbyshire. In both cases, 'lost' villages which had been drowned as the reservoirs had filled were exposed again. Other reservoirs, in the south and in Wales, dried up completely.

Figure 2.14 The drought in England and Wales, 1975-76 (left)

Figure 2.15 Water restrictions in England and Wales, August 1976 (centre)

Figure 2.16 Haweswater Reservoir (Lake District) during the 1976 drought

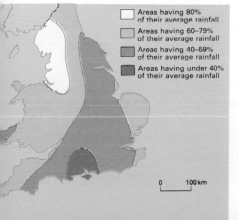

Areas having 80% of their average rainfall
Areas having 60–79% of their average rainfall
Areas having 40–69% of their average rainfall
Areas having under 40% of their average rainfall

0   100 km

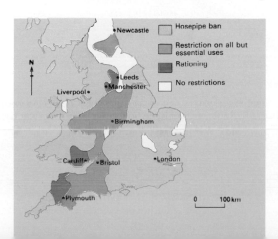

N

Hosepipe ban
Restriction on all but essential uses
Rationing
No restrictions

Newcastle
Leeds
Manchester
Liverpool
Birmingham
Cardiff   Bristol
London
Plymouth

0   100 km

⭘ WIND

Although Britain does not experience hurricanes, many areas are subjected to severe gales, especially in winter.

Winds affect us:

- At sea where they cause countless shipwrecks and loss of life, and threaten the security of oil-rigs and delay cross-Channel ferries.

- By flooding caused by strong winds which, if also associated with high spring tides, can cause storm surges up such tidal estuaries as the River Thames, or can breach coastal defences as at Towyn in North Wales in February 1990.

- By causing erosion, either by the winds driving huge waves on to cliffs and promenades, or by blowing away topsoil in the flat, hedgeless English Fenlands (Figure 3.20).

- By creating energy such as in the Orkneys where, with an annual average wind speed of 45 km per hour, Britain's first wind-powered generator was completed in time for the 1983/4 winter and which provides the islands with one-seventh of its energy needs. (Figure 6.23).

- By causing snow to drift.

The 'Great Storm' of 15/16 October 1987

This was the worst storm to affect South-east England since 1703. Although winds of similar strength are recorded annually in North-west Scotland they are given little attention by the media. The 'gale' of 1987 was considered important because it affected the centre of Britain's population and influence. Although several gusts reached hurricane force it did not have the characteristics of a hurricane. It developed so rapidly that its severity was not predicted in advance by the weather forecasters. Even at 1800 hours on 15 October it was thought to be an ordinary depression, with strong winds, moving up

Figure 2.18 Storm damage

the English Channel (Figure 2.17). The feature suddenly became much stronger and changed its route to pass over southern England. Twelve hours later, at 0600 hours on 16 October, it had reached the North Sea leaving 16 people dead, countless buildings and cars damaged, thousands of trees uprooted, fruit trees ruined, power and telephone lines cut (those in remote rural areas were not repaired for several days), roads and railways blocked; airports and channel ferry ports closed, and setting a new all-time record for insurance claims (Figure 2.18).

A storm of almost equal intensity affected all of Southern England on 25 January 1990. 47 people died. The greater loss of life was due to the wider area involved, and its daytime occurence when more people were out and about.

Storm-surges

These are rapid rises in the level of the sea which, at times of high spring tides, may break through coastal defences and flood low-lying land. The worst storm-surge to affect Eastern England, and the Netherlands, in recent times was during 31 January to 1 February 1953. The low pressure of a deep depression caused water to be pushed outwards towards coastal areas while the gale-force northerly winds formed large

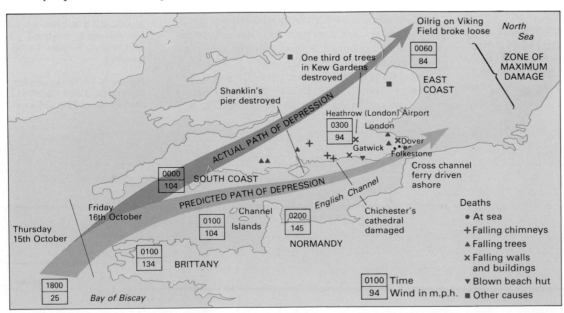

Figure 2.17 The 'Great Storm' October 1987

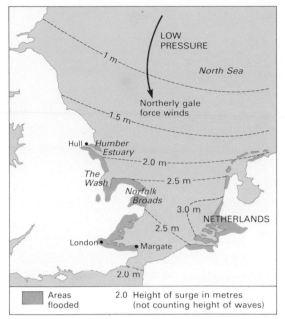

Figure 2.19 The storm surge, January 31/February 1, 1953

waves. As water was forced into the southern parts of the North Sea, which became both narrower and shallower, it piled up to give an extra large high tide (Figure 2.19). The event occurred at the same time as rivers, which were in flood, were trying to discharge extra water into the sea. Large areas between the Humber estuary and Margate were flooded, 307 people were drowned and 30 000 made homeless (The corresponding figures for the Netherlands were 1800 and 300 000). Although a storm-surge of this size may only occur once in every thousand years, it was decided that more efficient defences should be built. One outcome was the construction of the Thames Barrier (Figure 2.20).

A similar event, fortunately without any loss of life, occurred in North Wales in late February 1990.

Figure 2.20 The Thames Barrier at Woolwich. Hydraulic arms, housed in the piers, raise or lower the gates according to the level of the tide.

Snow and ice

Heavy falls of snow and the formation of ice can disrupt people's normal way of life. Under extreme conditions both can cause loss of life. The areas most prone to snow are the Scottish Highlands and the east coast of England. Salt is used for de-icing to try to limit ice formation, and to reduce the cost of snow clearance (Figure 2.21) and the risk of accidents. Some effects of heavy snowfalls are given in Figure 2.22. Frost, especially when it occurs in late spring, can kill fruit blossom as it tends to form in hollows.

Figure 2.21 Snow clearance

Figure 2.22 The effects of snow and ice

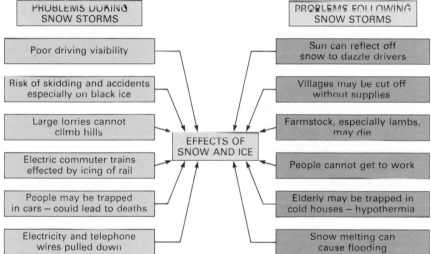

PROBLEMS DURING SNOW STORMS	PROBLEMS FOLLOWING SNOW STORMS
Poor driving visibility	Sun can reflect off snow to dazzle drivers
Risk of skidding and accidents especially on black ice	Villages may be cut off without supplies
Large lorries cannot climb hills	Farmstock, especially lambs, may die
Electric commuter trains effected by icing of rail	People cannot get to work
People may be trapped in cars – could lead to deaths	Elderly may be trapped in cold houses – hypothermia
Electricity and telephone wires pulled down	Snow melting can cause flooding

EFFECTS OF SNOW AND ICE

Fog and smog

This usually disrupts transport by grounding aircraft and closing airports, by causing serious road accidents — especially motorway pile-ups (Figure 2.23) — and by catching out unwary mountain-walkers. When smoke and dirt mix with fog in industrial areas, smog is formed.

The sulphur dioxide in the four-day London smog of 1952 left 4000 people dead or dying. Since then most British cities have introduced 'clean air zones' whereby factories and households are only allowed to burn smokeless fuel.

Figure 2.23 A motorway pile-up in fog, Ridgemont, Bedfordshire

○ RECENT CHANGES

Farming is an essential industry because it is:

- The source of most of our food and many of our raw materials.
- The major type of land use covering most of the inhabited Earth's surface.
- The major form of livelihood for over half of the world's people.
- A major contributor to world trade.

The farming industry

In 1958 the numbers of tractors and horses on British farms were about equal. By 1980 tractors had almost entirely replaced the horse. Farming is an industry and, like other industries, it has become increasingly mechanised. Some machines, like combine harvesters, save time and labour, others, which collect peas or potatoes, eliminate back-breaking jobs. Likewise, in the same way as industry needs factories, so farming requires its modern dairy parlours and broiler sheds (Figure 3.1). Most eggs are produced in battery units, with multiple tiers of cages. Broiler houses, which do not have cages, are used for rearing chickens for their meat. In both cases, temperature, light, humidity and the amount of feed are all automatically controlled — a task which is increasingly performed by computers. While this method of farming is regarded by many people as cruel and immoral, it is efficient and can reduce costs to the shopper by up to 50%.
Similarly in the modern milking parlour, cows are fed automatically while being machine-milked. The milk is then pumped directly into individual containers (to show how much each cow has produced) and then into refrigerated tanks to await collection by the tanker lorry.

Changes in the size of farms and fields

As machinery gets more expensive, farmers who can afford it, will try to buy up land and farms from their neighbours. This is because the cost of the new machinery may only be recovered and justified by creating larger economic units. The size of fields is increased by the removal of hedges, a move which while it benefits farmers, is frequently attacked for environmental reasons (page 27). The extensive fields of parts of Eastern England now have a prairie-like appearance (Figure 3.2).

Decrease in numbers employed in agriculture

In the Middle Ages, most people in Britain were employed directly in or were associated with agriculture. Increased mechanisation, urbanisation and industrialisation has caused this labour force

Figure 3.1(a) Battery hens

Figure 3.1(b) Intensive pig farming

to fall dramatically (Figure 3.3). The regional variation in the numbers employed in agriculture is shown in Figure 3.4.

Figure 3.2 Large scale farming

Changes in tenure

Many farms are still family owned but, as the expense of buying and running a farm grows, an increasing number are being run by food processing companies (e.g. frozen food firms in East Anglia and the East Midlands). The term **agribusiness** is used to describe those farms which are run and managed like factories.

Improved yields

These have been achieved by:

- An increase in the use of fertiliser and pesticides (page 26).
- Better strains and faster-growing seeds.
- Improved breeds and the use of vaccines.

Figure 3.3 Numbers employed in agriculture in the UK

	Year	1947	1959	1971	1983	1986
Number ('000s)		842	617	410	326	307
% of total UK working force		4.0	2.7	1.9	1.5	1.25

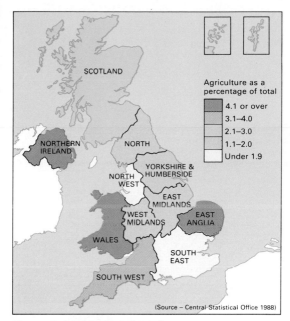

Figure 3.4 Agricultural workers as a percentage of the total workforce

Map legend:

Agriculture as a percentage of total

- 4.1 or over
- 3.1–4.0
- 2.1–3.0
- 1.1–2.0
- Under 1.9

(Source – Central Statistical Office 1988)

Organic farming

Between 1985 and 1989 over one thousand British farms, including that of the Prince of Wales, reverted to organic farming. This method of farming avoids the use of artificial fertiliser and pesticides using, instead, animal manure and compost. Yields, and therefore profits, may drop for the first year or two but then, as the quality of the soil and drainage improves, output rises and the cost of inputs (page 21) decrease.

Political pressures

Since 1939 Britain has tried to produce more of its own food not only to keep down the cost of imports, but to be as self-sufficient as possible. During the Second World War many chalkland areas were ploughed up to grow crops; these still remain as cereal-growing areas.

Many British farmers have only been able to grow certain crops and keep certain animals because successive governments have provided subsidies and grants. For example, farmers are guaranteed an agreed price for their milk or eggs. Without grants (an assured income) farmers would be unlikely to afford the new, large, specialist farm buildings and machinery. Since joining the EC in the early 1970's Britain has been subject to the Common Agricultural Policy by which all member countries have had to agree to certain prices and output. EC subsidies were responsible for large food surpluses in several commodities — the so-called 'mountains' (grain, beef, butter) and 'lakes' (wine, olive oil). During the late 1980s the EC has reduced quotas on which subsidies are paid. While this has lowered the surpluses it has also meant many specialist farmers, and those in marginal areas, have been forced out of business (e.g. dairy and sheep farmers).

Changes in land use

The reduction in subsidies discussed above has caused some British farmers to change to a different type of land use (e.g. the Farm Woodland scheme), while others, since 1989, are being paid, under the set-aside scheme, to take land out of production.

Changes in eating habits

These changes have come about because of:

- Refrigeration and an increase in frozen foods.
- An increase in the number of women in paid employment leading to more convenience food being consumed.
- Demand for processed, dried and tinned foods has risen.
- The desire, throughout the year, for fresh fruit and vegetables.
- A decrease in meat eating and an increase in health foods.
- Food health scares (e.g. salmonella and BSE).

Competition for land

Farmland, often of high quality, in the 'rural-urban' fringe (the outskirts of large cities) is in demand for housing, transport and industry. In more remote rural areas competition to use land other than for farming comes from tourism, forestry, quarrying, reservoirs and military requirements. Such competition increases the price of land.

Depopulation of rural areas

This change has gone on for nearly two centuries, and results from the increase in mechanisation causing a decrease in farm labour, the attraction of better paid city jobs, and the lack of social amenities in rural areas (e.g. schools). Figure 3.5 shows the results of rural depopulation in Scotland. In less remote, yet still areas of marginal farmland, farming may become a part-time occupation with farmers having to supplement their income by providing, for example, bed and breakfast or camp sites. The increased cost of housing, affordable only to wealthy city dwellers as 'holiday homes', forces younger members of the farming community off the land.

**Figure 3.5
An abandoned croft on
St. Kilda**

FARMING TYPES AND SYSTEMS

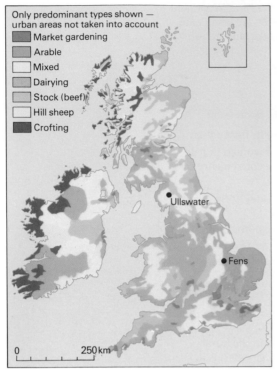

Only predominant types shown — urban areas not taken into account

- Market gardening
- Arable
- Mixed
- Dairying
- Stock (beef)
- Hill sheep
- Crofting

Ullswater

Fens

0   250 km

Figure 3.6 Types of farming in Britain

With so many people living in a relatively small area it is essential that British farming is made to be as efficient as possible. As a result, certain areas have specialised in one particular type of farming which is best suited to the local climate, soils and relief. These main farming areas are shown in Figure 3.6. However, it must be noted that local variations will occur within those main areas. For example, a hill sheep farmer in the southern Brecon Beacons may keep some dairy cows and grow some vegetables in the valley area for sale in the nearby urban markets of South Wales.

Figure 3.7 Typical sheep farming area in the Lake District (Martindale). Compare this with the landscape sketch in Figure 3.11

The West remains predominantly grassland with small fields and high hedges, having experienced less change, less mechanisation and less specialisation. However, some farms exceed 800 hectares. Figure 3.7 shows a Lake District valley.

Figure 3.8 Bulb cultivation in the Lincolnshire Fens

Central areas tend to be mixed farming landscapes with hedges and traditional forms of farming still visible, but in this area more mechanised and specialist farms are to be found. Many farms are under 100 hectares in size.

The East is given over to intensive arable land with few hedges and trees. The farms are usually situated in an area of level land, with large fields, open countryside and are highly mechanised, usually between 200-400 hectares in size. Figure 3.8 shows intensive land use in the Fenlands.

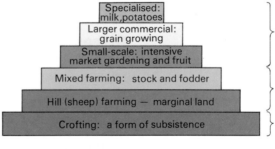

Specialised: milk, potatoes
Larger commercial: grain growing
Small-scale: intensive market gardening and fruit
Mixed farming: stock and fodder
Hill (sheep) farming — marginal land
Crofting: a form of subsistence

Personal needs less important than the demands of large urban markets

Personal needs with some surplus for sale

Personal needs dominant; little surplus for sale

Figure 3.9 The farming hierachy

A farming hierarchy

Figure 3.9 is an attempt to 'grade' the types of farming into a pyramid with the least specialised and least profit making at the base, and the most specialised and profitable at the peak. Compare the map (Figure 3.6) with maps of Britain which show highland; annual rainfall (Figure 2.1); length of growing season (Figure 2.4); and warmest summers (Figure 2.5). You will also need an atlas map which shows the largest centres of population.

Can you now:

1 Describe where each of the main types of farming are to be found, and then give reasons for its location in that area?

2 Define such terms as 'subsistence', 'commercial', 'intensive', 'extensive', 'arable', 'pastoral', 'mixed farming', 'market gardening' and 'crofting'?

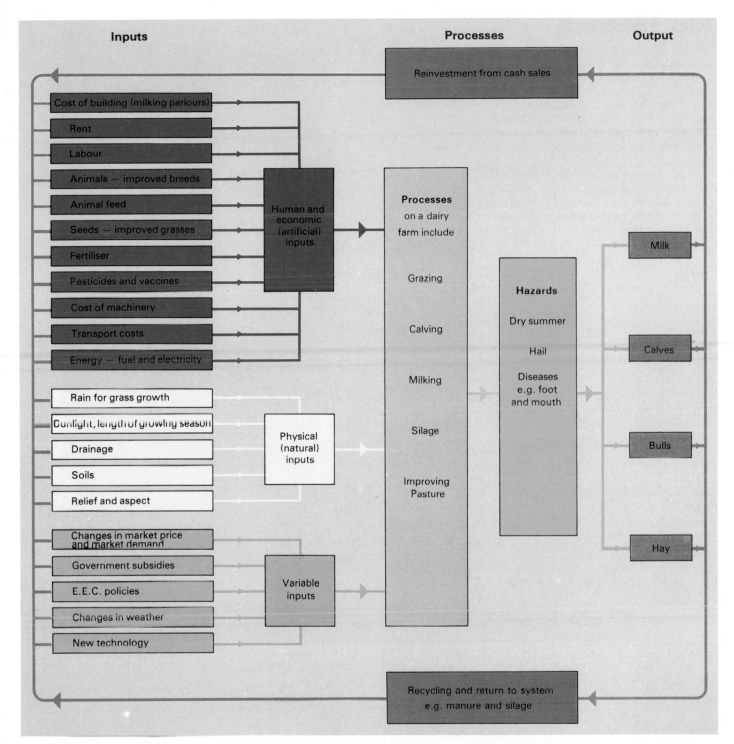

Figure 3.10 The farming system (based on a dairy farm)

Farming systems

It has already been stated that farming is an industry, and like an industry it has **inputs** into the farm, **processes** which take place on the farm, and **outputs**.

Inputs include the physical environment (natural inputs) such as climate, soils and relief, together with human (artificial) inputs.

Processes are the methods of farming, such as growing crops or rearing animals.

Outputs are the farm products available for sale.

These must be greater in monetary terms than the inputs if the farmer is to make a profit.

Figure 3.10 shows how this 'systems approach' works in a typical British dairy farm. Study the diagram and try to explain what it shows. Can you now apply this 'systems approach' to make a similar model for your own local farm? Do you think that physical constraints (inputs) are less important today than in the past? And that human and economic factors are more important than in previous decades?

HILL FARMING

In order that cereal crops may grow, the land must be well drained and flat enought to take the weight of modern combine harvesters, together with a climate that gives low rainfall and plenty of sun. The proportion of land in Cumbria, for example, which fulfils these physical conditions is small. With a rainfall rising to over 2500 mm in the central Lake District, and the cool summers, this means that the climate, together with the relief and the skill of the Cumbrian farmers unite to grow grass which is second to none. While the valleys are populated by over half a million cattle, the higher and more remote areas contain over one and a half million sheep.

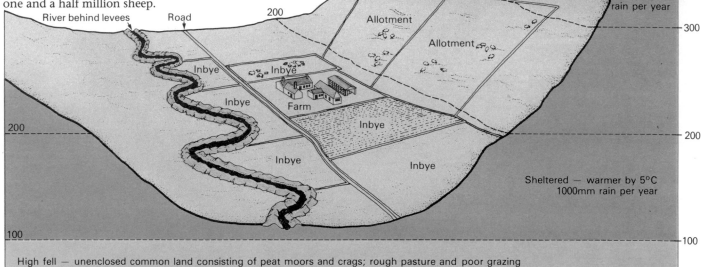

High fell — unenclosed common land consisting of peat moors and crags; rough pasture and poor grazing

Allotment (or intake) — enclosed rough grazing on the lower fell

Inbye — low lying land near to farmhouse; grazing, grass conservation (hay and silage) and sheep in lambing season

Figure 3.11 A hill farm in the Lake District

	January	February	March	April	May	June	July	August	Sept	October	Nov	Dec
The sheep farmer's year	Ewes on fell, weaker animals on allotments		Flock gathered	Lambing on inbye land	Fell	Return to inbye for short periods for and dipping		shearing	Surplus ewes and lambs sold	On high fells	Dipping and mating	Return to fell
Location	High fell		Allotment	Inbye	Fell	Inbye and allotment			Fell	Fell	Inbye	Fell
Intensive work												
Time for other jobs												

Figure 3.12 The farmer's year in the Lake District

The plan of a typical hill farm is shown in Figure 3.11 and a photograph illustrating the three types of land is seen in Figure 3.7. The farmer's year (Figure 3.12) shows periods of intensive hard work, separated by intervals during which the farmer has relatively little to do and could be free to do other jobs. Recently, hill farmers in all of Britain have been badly hit by:

- A drop in prices for sheep and sheep products.
- In 1970, the sale of 165 lambs would have enabled the farmer to buy 1 tractor. In 1980, 330 lambs would have enabled the farmer to buy 1 tractor.
- Up to a 100% increase in the cost of fuel and fodder.
- Several severe winters and poor summers.
- Fall-out from the Chernobyl accident.

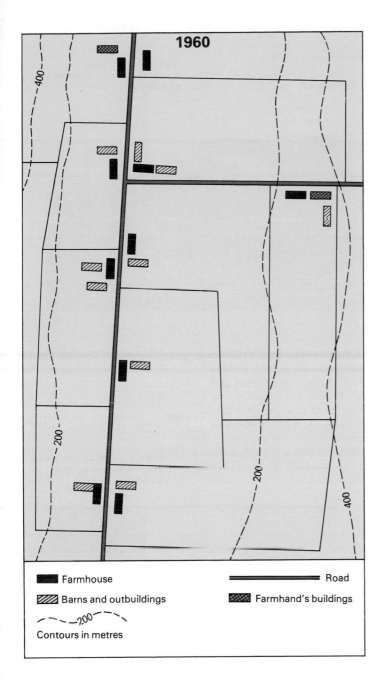

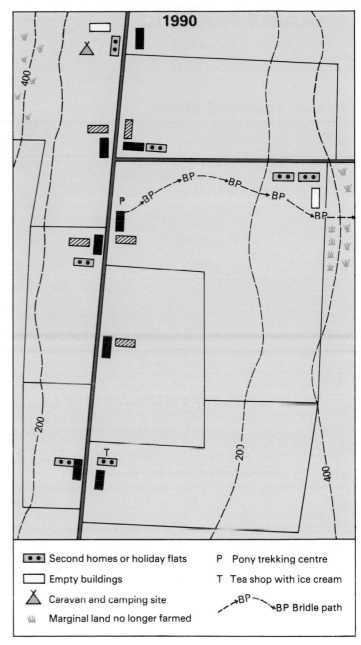

◼ Farmhouse	▬▬▬ Road
▨ Barns and outbuildings	▧ Farmhand's buildings
⌒⌒ 200 ⌒⌒ Contours in metres	

⊡⊡ Second homes or holiday flats	P Pony trekking centre
☐ Empty buildings	T Tea shop with ice cream
◬ Caravan and camping site	⋙ BP ⋙ BP Bridle path
⅗ Marginal land no longer farmed	

Changes

As a result of falling sheep prices, increased costs in running the hill farm, and several poor years of unreliable weather, changes have been forced upon the farmer. Some of these changes have been shown in Figure 3.13. By carefully studying each year, you should be able to notice six such changes:

1 Some amalgamation of smaller farms.
2 Some marginal land is no longer being used.
3 Fewer farmhands are needed (due to increased mechanisation) and so their former cottages are used as second homes.
4 The opening of a caravan and camping site.
5 Pony trekking as a side-line.

6 A tea room and ice cream shop have opened.

What the diagrams do not show is the extra financial aid which both the British Government and, especially, the EC have had to give to help British hill farmers.

Finally, from the information given on these two pages, you should be able to:

1 Draw your own diagram showing the hill farming system (refer to Figure 3.10) which will include the farmer's inputs, the processes and hazards on the farm, and the final outputs.

2 Explain why British hill farmers are finding it increasingly difficult to make a profit and to earn a living.

Figure 3.13 Changes in hill farming. Map A shows the farm in 1960; Map B shows the same farm in 1990

◉ ARABLE FARMING

East Anglia, together with the Fens, has the most mechanised and profitable farming system in Britain.

Physical (natural) inputs

Relief

The land is, by British standards, almost flat (Figures 3.14 and 3.8), and this encourages the use of labour-saving machines.

Figure 3.14 Large-scale farming in East Anglia

Soils

In this area soils are deep and rich in nutrients, being mainly boulder clay (which has been left by glaciers) lying on top of chalk. These give good anchorage for the roots of cereal crops and give high yields although they do tend to be poor for drainage.

Rainfall

With a rainfall of under 650 mm a year, this is the driest part of Britain and the most suitable for cereals. Fortunately there is a summer rainfall maximum which coincides with the growing season, although in most years sprinklers are needed for any vegetables and soft fruit.

Temperatures

The cold winters break up the soil, and the warm, sunny summers ripen the crops.

Human (artificial) inputs

Fertiliser

For centuries 'marling' (adding lime) has been carried out to try to lighten the soil and so improve its drainage. Today new types of fertilisers have doubled crop yields.

Mechanisation

Each farm may have several combine harvesters, potato pickers (Figure 3.15) and pea-mobiles to reduce human labour.

Figure 3.15 Farm mechanisation - a potato picker

Crop rotation

If the same crop is grown in the same field every year, the same plant foods are taken out of the soil, and this could also allow insect pests and diseases to build up, thereby lowering the crop yield. To prevent this, the farmer **rotates** the crops (Figure 3.16). Sugar beet, peas and beans help to put nutrients back into the soil which are then used up by wheat and barley. The traditional four-year rotation has now been replaced by a six- or seven-year rotation.

Figure 3.16 Seven-year crop rotation in East Anglia

Year One	1.	2.	3.
1 = Field number	Peas or beans	Winter wheat	Potatoes
4.	5.	6.	7.
Winter wheat or barley	Sugar beet	Grass	Grass (Two year ley i.e. grass grown as a crop)

Year Two	1.	2.	3.
All rotate by one field	Grass	Peas or beans	Winter wheat
4.	5.	6.	7.
Potatoes	Winter wheat or barley	Sugar beet	Grass

Seeds and pesticides

These have both improved in quality, and seeds are increasingly disease-resistant.

Marketing

This has had to be improved so that many products are fresh when they arrive at the market (e.g. milk, fruit, peas).

Government help

Farmers are given grants for fertilisers and drainage, lower interest rates for new machines and buildings, and subsidies for their wheat, barley, sugar beet and milk.

Many East Anglian farms may concentrate on cereals (wheat and barley), but root crops are also important (potatoes, sugar beet, peas and beans). Farmers also plant considerable areas with grass to support herds of dairy or beef cattle.

◎ FARM MANAGEMENT

Just as farmers have to consider the time, distance and cost factors in deciding what they should grow or rear, they have also to consider these same factors in their own farm management so that their daily movements are kept to a minimum.

The farmer as a decision maker

The farm in Figure 3.17 is typical for East Anglia and shows how in one particular year, the farmer organised the crops and animals. Remembering the need to rotate the use of fields why do you think the farmer decided to:

1 grow cereals in the largest fields,
2 grow cereals furthest from the farmhouse,
3 keep dairy cows near to the farmhouse,
4 keep most of his dairy cows to the east of the main road,
5 leave the field next to the river as grass,
6 put store cattle on this field,
7 leave two fields just as grass with no cattle in them,
8 grow peas and beans near to the farm,
9 grow peas, beans and potatoes near to the main road,
10 grow crops (e.g. sugar beet) in adjacent fields?

Marketing of produce

Time, distance and cost also affect where the outputs from this farm are sold. For example:

- Potatoes will be sold locally because they are bulky.
- Peas and beans will go to a local frozen food factory as they must arrive fresh.
- Sugar beet must also be refined locally as it is bulky.
- Wheat and barley can be sent further away because they will keep longer and the demand for their processed products is in larger, distant, urban markets.

Figure 3.17 Farm management on an East Anglian farm

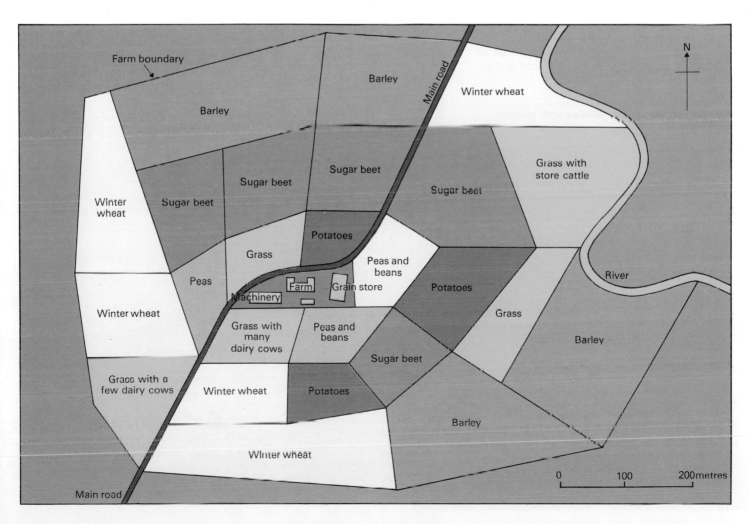

FARMING AND THE ENVIRONMENT

The use of chemicals

Fertiliser is a mineral compound containing one or more of the main six elements needed for plant growth. The average soil does not contain sufficient quantities of the essential nutrients (especially the three most significant ones of nitrogen, phosporous and potassium) to provide either a healthy crop or an economic yield. To overcome these deficiencies fertiliser, especially nitrate and phosphate, is added. There is increasing concern when nitrate, in particular, is leached and transported by throughflow into rivers and lakes. Three of these concerns are:

1 **Economic** as the loss of nitrate from farmland means the farmer will have to buy both the expensive fertiliser and the machinery with which to apply it (Figure 3.18).

2 **Ecological** as nitrate will act as a fertiliser in streams and lakes causing a rapid growth of algae (Figure 3.19) and other plants. Both the living and decaying plants use up much of the oxygen in the water leaving insufficient for fish life.

3 **Human health** if drinking water supplies have high levels of nitrate. Levels are highest, exceeding the EC recommended upper limit, in the arable areas of East Anglia, Fenland and the East Midlands.

Figure 3.18 Spreading nitrates with modern machinery

Phosphate in water can also affect plant growth. The major sources of phosphate are farm slurry (animal dung) and untreated sewage. Slurry is 100 times more polluting than household sewage.

Pesticide is defined as all chemicals applied to crops to control pests, disease and weeds. These can also affect wildlife although direct poisonings are usually due to their careless, rather than deliberate, use.

Burning straw

Although the ploughing back of straw (after the harvested crops have been removed) returns nutrients to the soil, it may clog up machinery as well as increasing labour costs and limiting the growth of new roots. If straw is burnt fungal spores and weed seeds are destroyed to give a cleaner soil. However this burning does create air pollution, reduces visibility for road users, harms wildlife and damages hedgerows and trees. Restrictions on burning are already in force, and a total ban is predicted in the near future.

Figure 3.19 Algae forming in a river as a result of a high nitrate level

Removal of hedgerows

Between 1945 and 1975 25% of British hedgerows disappeared (over 45% in Norfolk). Throughout the 1980's an estimated 8000 km a year were removed. Farmers remove hedgerows and trees to create larger fields (Figure 3.2) as hedgerows are costly and time-consuming to maintain, they take up space which could be used for crops and they limit the size of machinery. Trees get in the way of new mechanised hedgetrimmers. Yet the destruction of hedgerows can harm the environment as there are fewer roots to bind the soil together leaving it exposed to running water and, in Eastern England, the wind (Figure 3.20). Wildlife in the form of plants, insects, birds and animals lose their natural habitat, and many people feel that the landscape becomes less attractive. Figure 3.21 shows the advantages of a well maintained hedgerow.

Draining wetlands

Wetlands are transition zones between land and water where the soil is frequently waterlogged and the water table is at, or near to, the surface. They form one of Britain's few remaining natural environments, yet 90% of those in existence 40 years ago have since been drained. The largest remaining wetland in Britain is the Norfolk Broads but this is under threat from among others, farmers. Land has been drained for pastureland. Reeds have been cleared, or are dying, leaving fewer habitats for wildlife. As more river banks are exposed they are washed away by waves caused by passing leisure boats. The use of modern pumps to remove water has led to the peaty soils 'shrinking' and the land falling to below river-levels. Flood banks, many of which need urgent repairs, have had to be built to prevent flooding, especially at times of high tide and storm surges (page 17).

Following a three-year experimental scheme the government did create, in 1988, six 'Environmentally Sensitive Areas' (ESAs), one of which includes the Halvergate Marshes on the Norfolk Broads. Each ESA is considered to be important for its landscape, historic and habitat value. Farmers are offered two levels of payment. The lower level is for maintaining the present landscape, the higher one for making environmental improvements such as replanting hedges and restoring ponds.

Figure 3.20 Soil erosion by the wind, Longworth, Oxfordshire

Figure 3.21 A carefully maintained hedgerow

○ ECOSYSTEMS

In prehistoric times most of Britain was part of a woodland ecosystem consisting of such deciduous trees as oak, ash, birch and beech. An ecosystem is a natural system (Figure 1.1) in which the life cycles of plants (flora) and animals (fauna) are linked to each other and to the non-living environment.

The non-living environment includes:

- Water — either in the form of rain or from water stored in the soil.

- Air — providing oxygen, essential for all life, and carbon dioxide.

- Solar energy — the sun being the earth's primary source of energy as well as providing heat and light.

- Rocks — whose rates of weathering may vary and which might be either permeable (allowing water to pass through them) or impermeable.

- Soils — which vary in depth, acidity, nutrients and fertility.

An ecosystem can vary in size from an individual oak tree up to an oak woodland or extensive continental forests. Any ecosystem depends upon two basic processes — the flow of energy and the recycling of materials. Energy is transferred by means of the food chain in which there are four hierarchal levels.

A typical ecosystem for a British woodland is shown in Figure 4.1. As in any system the woodland has inputs, processes and stores, and outputs. Most natural ecosystems have been altered by human activity.

Development

When Britain's population began to grow, forests were cut down to clear the land for farming and for use as fuel, for building, for smelting iron, and the building of ships (one ship in Elizabethan times used 2000 trees). When Britain's industrial revolution came, and before coal was used, vast areas of forest were cleared, and wood was used for charcoal. The population growth of the nineteenth century created such a demand for food, that many more trees were uprooted to make room for crops, and to build more ships for carrying people out to colonise the Empire, and to bring back food and raw materials.

The First World War further denuded the forests until many areas looked like the one shown in Figure 4.2. As a result, in 1919, the Forestry Commission was set up to begin a replanting programme. But their planting programme did not meet Britain's growing demand for timber products, and the Second World War only worsened the situation.

Figure 4.2 Demand for timber and the need for more agricultural land resulted in some areas losing their tree cover — the Cheviot Hills in the Northumberland National Park

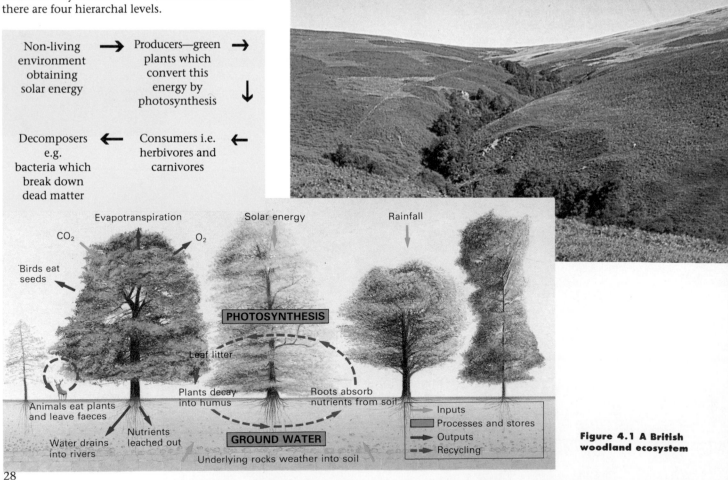

Non-living environment obtaining solar energy → Producers—green plants which convert this energy by photosynthesis →

Decomposers e.g. bacteria which break down dead matter ← Consumers i.e. herbivores and carnivores ←

Evapotranspiration

CO_2 O_2

Solar energy   Rainfall

Birds eat seeds

PHOTOSYNTHESIS

Leaf litter

Plants decay into humus

Roots absorb nutrients from soil

Animals eat plants and leave faeces

Nutrients leached out

Water drains into rivers

GROUND WATER

Underlying rocks weather into soil

Inputs
Processes and stores
Outputs
Recycling

Figure 4.1 A British woodland ecosystem

The Forestry Act of 1967 and the Countryside Act of 1968 gave the Forestry Commissioners the job of:

- Promoting the interest of forestry.
- Developing areas of afforestation and the production and supply of timber and other forest products. (Figure 4.3.)
- Maintaining adequate reserves of growing trees.
- Controlling timber pests and diseases.
- Providing tourist, recreational and sporting facilities.

The location of Britain's forests

By 1988, 9.9% of Great Britain was forested (Figure 4.4) — low by EC standards (22%). Most areas were primarily upland moorlands of low value grazing. The soils were often peat lying on top of a cold wet sticky boulder clay. Figure 4.5 shows several other reasons for the location of forests, while Figures 4.6 to 4.8 show how mechanised forestry has become.

Figure 4.3 Afforestation on a large scale carried out by the Forestry Commission in the Kielder Forest, Northumberland

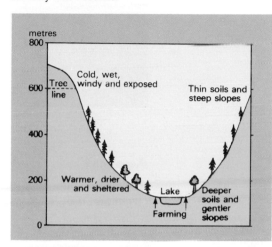

Figure 4.5 Growing conditions for coniferous trees

Figure 4.6 Chainsaws are now used exclusively for felling trees

Figure 4.7 This 'forwarder' is able to harvest shortwood with only minimal damage to agricultural land.

Figure 4.4 Major forest areas in Great Britain

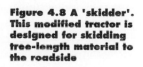

Figure 4.8 A 'skidder'. This modified tractor is designed for skidding tree-length material to the roadside

○ AFFORESTATION

Not everybody favours the mass re-clothing of upland valleys and moorlands with conifers. The poet, William Wordsworth, wrote of the larch: 'Ten thousand of this spiky tree are stuck in at once upon the side of a hill ... they can grow up into nothing but deformity'. Do you agree? Perhaps you can think of your own reasons for and against afforestation. If so, check your list with the ideas below. You may well have added to the list. It is also important that you can appreciate both sides of the argument and then make your own decision as to which one you favour.

Figure 4.9 A well-planned forest at Tarn Hows, Cumbria

For

- It helps to meet Britain's increasing demand for timber and forest products.
- It reduces the cost of imports and a dependence upon overseas producers. In 1980 timber and its associated products were Britain's second most expensive import (after food), and Britain produced less than 10% of its total needs. Foreign producers such as the USSR, Canada and Scandinavia want to sell to Britain more expensive, processed products than the relatively cheaper untreated timber.
- Soil erosion is avoided as trees prevent rapid run-off after heavy rainfall. They also prevent the silting up of reservoirs.
- The risk of flooding caused by rapid run-off is reduced.
- Tourism is encouraged by including picnic areas, camping sites and nature trails.
- Jobs are provided in areas of limited employment. Forestry can create six jobs to every one in farming in upland marginal land.
- The beauty of an area is enhanced by careful landscaping.
- Wild life is preserved and this encourages visitors.
- Trees provide oxygen which is necessary for life on earth.
- Trees planted in the relatively mild British climate mature five times faster than those in Canada, Russia or Scandinavia.
- Britain's own supply can be drawn upon, since Third World countries are gradually developing and increasing their own demands for timber as well as charging higher prices.

Against

- Blanket planting (i.e. row upon row of uniform trees) spoils the 'natural wildscape' landscape.
- Land which was previously used for sheep farming, grouse moors and walking, is now used as forest land.
- It is cheaper to import timber and pulp from Canada and Scandinavia than to produce our own.
- It increases the risk of fires.
- In return for high capital investment, it provides very few jobs. The government claims it costs £50 000 to create one job.
- Employment is seasonal in nature.
- It has a very slow return on investment — trees take 40 to 50 years to mature.
- It limits access for hikers and may reduce tourism.
- Coniferous trees are visually less attractive than deciduous.
- Coniferous forests let in little light and this discourages plant, bird and animal life. This causes protests from environmental bodies such as the RSPB.
- Forest herbicide chemicals (e.g. paraquat) can cause contamination of rivers and reservoirs and the depletion of fish stocks.
- Today there is little money available for further investment.
- Timber lorries damage and cause congeston rural roads.

Private forestry

The area of Great Britain under forest has been increasing slowly by 0.1% per year rising from 8.8% in 1977 to 9.8% in 1988. This increase has mainly been the result of the growth in private forestry. In 1977 the Forestry Commission planted 18.7 thousand hectares of new trees compared to 9.2 thousand hectares by private foresters. In 1987 the Forestry Commission only planted 13.3 thousand hectares while private foresters planted 23.6 thousand hectares. In the same period the share of privately owned forest increased from 40% to 51%.

Private development was encouraged by the giving of a grant for each hectare that was planted. These grants were given providing that:

- sound forestry practice was followed,
- forests were effectively integrated with agriculture,
- the environment was safeguarded,
- opportunities for public recreation were offered.

In some cases, and especially in the Highland Region of Scotland (Figure 14.10), this led to wealthy individuals buying plots of land. Through grants and tax relief, the Government paid up to three-quarters of the cost incurred by these individuals in planting conifers in the previously moorland landscape. The timber could be sold anytime after ten years giving a tax free profit to the individual and leaving the local ecosystem totally changed.

The Flow Country of Caithness and Sutherland

This area contains the largest natural 'blanket-bog' environment in Europe. It consists of vast open expanses of peat and pools, moss and rare flowers.

Figure 4.10 Private foresters in Northern Scotland

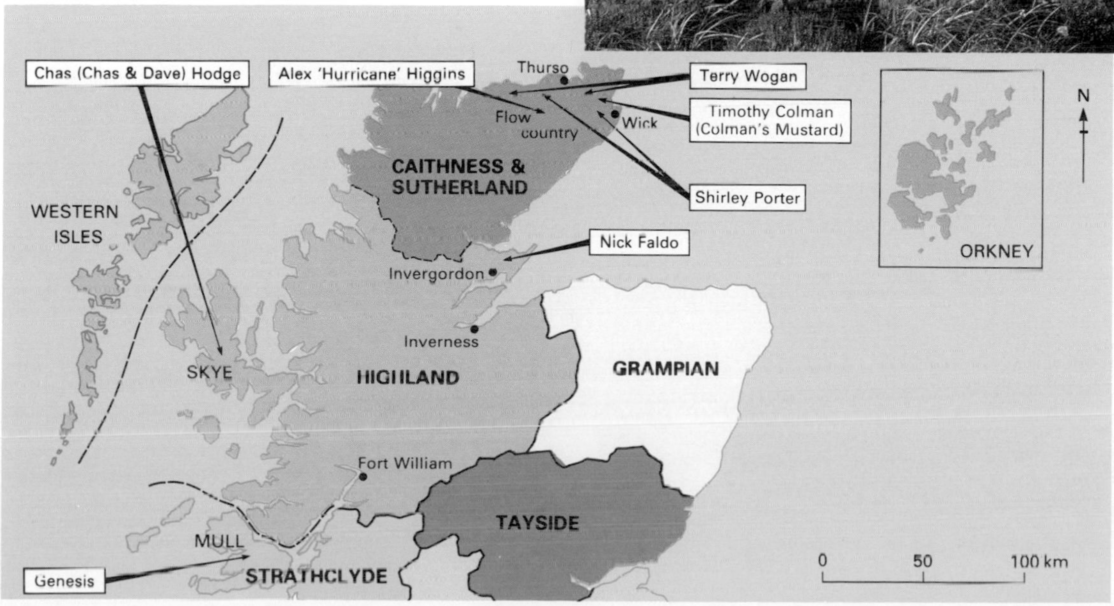

It forms a habitat and breeding ground for a wide variety of rare birds. It is recognised to be one of the world's few remaining outstanding 'natural' ecosystems being, in its way, as significant as the Brazilian rainforests and the African Serengeti. Yet despite being protected by four international treaties, it is disappearing under a blanket of forest at an alarming rate. These conifer plantations, mainly Sitka spruce, drive away communities of wildlife. Much of the area is unsuited to conifers (Figure 4.11) giving an economic return of under 1.3%.(The Forestry Commission consider a return of under 3% not to be worthwhile.)

The 1988 Government Budget eliminated these tax incentives for private investors. Instead, through the Forestry Commission's new Woodlands Grant Scheme, incentives four times greater are to be paid for planting deciduous rather than coniferous species. The aim is to encourage farmers in marginal areas to diversify into forestry in the light of falling prices and EC food surpluses, and to create multi-purpose woodlands integrating conservation and recreation.

Figure 4.11 Private forestry in the Flow Country of Caithness and Sutherland

○ LANDSCAPE QUALITY

Many early attempts at afforestation have been criticised for the lack of thought given to the resulting visual appearance of the forest. The so-called 'blanket planting' of one species of tree which accounts for hard, unnatural, straight lines has been attacked. Today much thought and planning goes into afforestation.

Some of the ideas used in 1980 are shown on Figure 4.12. Various people will view this landscape differently. What really matters is how much you think that this is a visually pleasing landscape. Some people still regarded it as too dark and unattractive to attract visitors or to be a habitat for wildlife. As the demand for increased recreational amenities grew during the 1980s, the cost of spraying trees to rid them of insect pests increased, and people's perception of the environment changed, the Forestry Commission has attempted new approaches. One of these, in the Kielder Forest in Northumberland (Figures 4.13 and 4.14), has attempted to improve the whole ecosystem rather than, as earlier, concentrating solely on landscaping the trees. In what ways do you think the ecosystem has been improved? What further improvements would you make?

Figure 4.13 Improving the environment in the Kielder Forest in the 1990s

Figure 4.12 Planning the landscape in an afforested area in the 1970s and 1980s

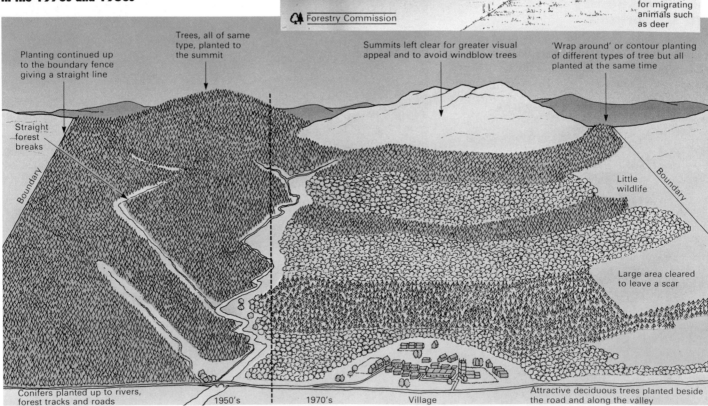

Trees planted at different times. Their differences in height are scientifically more attractive

Trees of different species and with a lower density encourage more bird life which feeds on, and reduces insects and consequently the need for spaying

Summits left clear for Heather moorlands. Forms a habitat for wild goats, grouse and golden eagles

Only small areas cleared at a time to reduce 'scars'

Mature woodland forms a habitat for tawny owl, and provides food for short-eared owl

Cleared forest branches left to rot. Takes 10 years. Nutrients returned to the soil

Winding forest road

Ponds created

Land 100 metres wide cleared of conifers and left as a mixture of grass, conifers and the more attractive decisuous

River North Tyne

Forestry Commission

Land next to river left clear for migrating animals such as deer

Planting continued up to the boundary fence giving a straight line

Trees, all of same type, planted to the summit

Summits left clear for greater visual appeal and to avoid windblow trees

'Wrap around' or contour planting of different types of tree but all planted at the same time

Straight forest breaks

Boundary

Boundary

Little wildlife

Large area cleared to leave a scar

Conifers planted up to rivers, forest tracks and roads

1950's

1970's

Village

Attractive deciduous trees planted beside the road and along the valley

Figure 4.14 Kielder Forest

◉ RECREATIONAL USE

Four main types of recreational demand can be recognised:

1 Day visitors need car parks, picnic areas, forest trails and information centres (Figures 4.15 and 4.16).
2 Overnight visitors use camp sites and tourist cabins.
3 Specialist activities need to be provided for, such as pony trekking, cycling, fishing, car rallies, orienteering, and wildlife study.
4 Organised school and scientific parties require the necessary facilities. Amenities are usually spread out to avoid congestion, unless there is a demand for such facilities as picnic areas, toilets and information centres around a car park. Recreation rarely comes into conflict with timber production, but conflict can occur between different types of recreation e.g. horse riding and walking.

In order to develop the full recreational potential of forests, the Forestry Commission has created eight forest parks (Figure 4.4) including the New Forest.

Forestry's problems in the 1990s

■ Should the area of Britain covered by forest be increased?
■ Should Britain's imports be reduced or should Britain rely on cheaper products from abroad?
■ What can forestry do to try to create more employment?
■ Can forests be made an integral part of Britain's landscape?
■ Should Britain have its own pulp and paper industry?
■ Will forestry only be economical if given tax concessions?
■ What affect will the selling of Forestry Commission land to private owners have?

Figure 4.15 Provision is made for day-trippers to forests

Figure 4.16 Opportunities for recreation in Forestry Commission areas — Ennerdale Forest, Cumbria

○ THE WATER (HYDROLOGICAL) CYCLE

The water cycle is an example of a closed system (see page 4) in which water, either in a liquid or a vapour form, is used over and over again. Although some people claim that the cycle has inputs (precipitation) and outputs (evapotranspiration), in reality, the water is continually circulated by a series of transfers (Figure 5.1).

Interruptions in the transfer of water occur when it is held in storage as snow or in lakes and the ground. Occasional interruptions in the cycle occur when heavy snowfall or drought mean that less water can return to the sea or is available for evapotranspiration. Snowmelt and heavy rain will have the reverse effect.

Uses of water

Figure 5.2 shows some of the diverse uses of water. Figure 5.3 shows how the amount of water consumed per person in Britain has increased over the years (remember that the overall population has also increased considerably over the same period), and how much is used daily in the average home and in the manufacture of selected products.

The mismatch between supply and demand

On average between three and six cubic metres of rain per person per day falls over Britain. This is more than is needed but it does not always fall where and when it is needed. The resultant problems include:

Figure 5.1 The water (hydrological) cycle

■ Irregular rainfall. Sometimes there may be several months of drought while at other times excess rain causes flooding and the surplus is quickly returned by rivers and 'lost' into the sea.

■ During winter the supply of rainfall exceeds demand whereas in summer, when temperatures are higher, demand exceeds supply.

Figure 5.2 Publicity used by the Severn Water Authority

FOR DRINKING
or we die of thirst !!!

FOR GROWING FOOD
or we starve !

FOR WASHING —
OURSELVES

AND OUR BELONGINGS!

SWIMMING, FISHING OR BOATING

FOR INDUSTRY: POWER, COOLING, CARRYING, MAKING OR CLEANING
Our JOBS depend on it !!

Figure 5.3 Demands for water

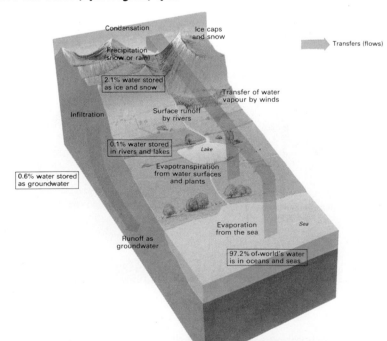

Condensation
Ice caps and snow
Precipitation (snow or rain)
2.1% water stored as ice and snow
Transfers (flows)
Transfer of water vapour by winds
Infiltration
Surface runoff by rivers
0.1% water stored in rivers and lakes
Lake
0.6% water stored as groundwater
Evapotranspiration from water surfaces and plants
Evaporation from the sea
Sea
Runoff as groundwater
97.2% of world's water is in oceans and seas

Growing demand for Water

	Amount of water consumed per person per day in Great Britain
1830	18 litres
1929	126 litres
1980	330 litres
Domestic	140 litres
Non-domestic	190 litres

Major domestic uses

	Litres per person per day
Flushing lavatory	50
Washing and bathing	50
Laundry	14
Washing up	14
Car and Garden	9
Drinking and Cooking	3
Total	140

Examples of industrial demands

Litres needed	to produce one
450,000	Family car
400,000	Ton of paper
200,000	Ton of steel
180,000	Car tyre
300	Gallon of petrol
200	Pint of beer

- Most rain falls in the higher, less populated areas of the North and West (Figure 2.1) whereas the highest demand (by people, farming and industry) is in the Midlands, the South-east, and the lowlands on either side of the Pennines (Figure 5.4).
- Areas of highest demand change over the years as people and industries move.

As a result, water has to be stored in reservoirs, in areas where there is a water surplus and transferred, often across watersheds, to places which have a water deficiency (e.g. Kielder pages 36-37).

The functions of Water Authorities

The location of the ten Water Authorities covering England and Wales are shown on Figure 5.5. What are the names of the ten regional headquarters shown by a dot and their initial letter? The functions of these authorities, include:

1 To ensure that enough rainwater is collected, stored, treated, and piped to supply everyone (householders, farmers and industrialists).
2 To dispose of sewage and industrial waste.
3 To prevent river pollution.
4 To prevent floods and to drain the land.
5 To encourage fisheries and other river life.
6 To provide recreational amenities.

Despite the actions of Water Authorities many industries have to recycle their water, and several urban areas have to use retreated water. Once water has been used it may include chemicals (page 26), poisons, untreated sewage and waste. In 1989, prior to privatisation, it was claimed that the quality of water provided by most authorities was not up to EC health standards. During the drought of 1989 one authority in the South of England refused to buy water from Kielder because it was 'too dirty and expensive' while the next day stating that 'worms in its own supply were not harmful'.

The need for water management

Good management is needed to boost the quality and quantity of the water supply. Britain, unlike Third World countries, has the money to build dams, create reservoirs and introduce water transfer schemes. Modern schemes have to:

- attempt to manage the whole of the drainage basin,
- be multi-purpose to justify their huge costs and disruption to life.

Reservoirs should be large enough to store water for use (domestic and industrial) throughout the year, to generate energy (hydro-electricity), and to provide recreational facilities (e.g. sailing, nature reserves). They should also be able to regulate the

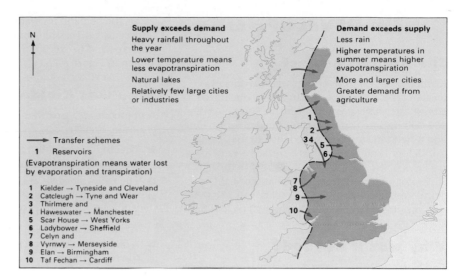

Figure 5.4 Location of major reservoirs in England and Wales

flow in the river holding back water to prevent flooding or releasing it to prevent levels getting too low.

Differing demands for water can cause conflicts

Competing demands can cause conflicts, both economic and environmental. Taking reservoirs as an example, certain groups of people will be in favour of their creation but other groups will be opposed to them.

Groups in favour may include:

- Householders in lowland areas which are short of water.
- Industrialists in the manufacturing regions of Britain.
- Recreational groups hoping for additional water activities.

Groups against may include:

- Local farmers and inhabitants liable to lose their land and homes.
- Tourists and locals, if access is denied, and conservationists, if plant and wildlife habitats are threatened.
- Local political groups (as in Wales) who feel that 'their' water should be paid for by consumers living outside the area.

Figure 5.5 The regional Water Authorities of England and Wales

● NEW DEVELOPMENTS

The Kielder project

Kielder Reservoir, one of the largest artificially created lakes in Europe, is situated in one of the largest artificially created forests in Europe — the 101 000 hectare (250 000 acre) Kielder Forest. One and a half million trees were felled to make way for Kielder Water which has a surface area of 1084 hectares (2684 acres) making it larger than Lake Ullswater and three-quarters the area of Lake Windermere. It has a storage capacity of 188 000 million litres (41 350 million gallons) (Figure 5.6).

Why was it needed?

The Northumbrian Water Authority is responsible for an area of about 930 000 hectares (3600 square miles), comprising the conurbation of Tyne and Wear, the Counties of Durham and Cleveland, most of the County of Northumberland, and parts of North Yorkshire and Cumbria. In the early 1970s the demand for water by industries (especially on Teesside) and for domestic purposes was expected to exceed supply by 1981. This is shown in Figure 5.7.

Why was Kielder chosen?

A number of reasons were put forward for choosing Kielder:

■ The limited agricultural value of the area, and the small number of inhabitants living there.

■ The valley narrows at this point.

■ The gradient upstream is relatively flat, allowing a maximum volume of water to collect there.

■ A band of volcanic rock (Whinsill) would help the foundations.

■ The large water catchment area.

■ Extensive local deposits of boulder clay, sand and gravel needed in the dam construction.

■ It is an area of heavy and reliable rainfall (1200 mm a year).

Figure 5.6 Aerial view of Kielder Water

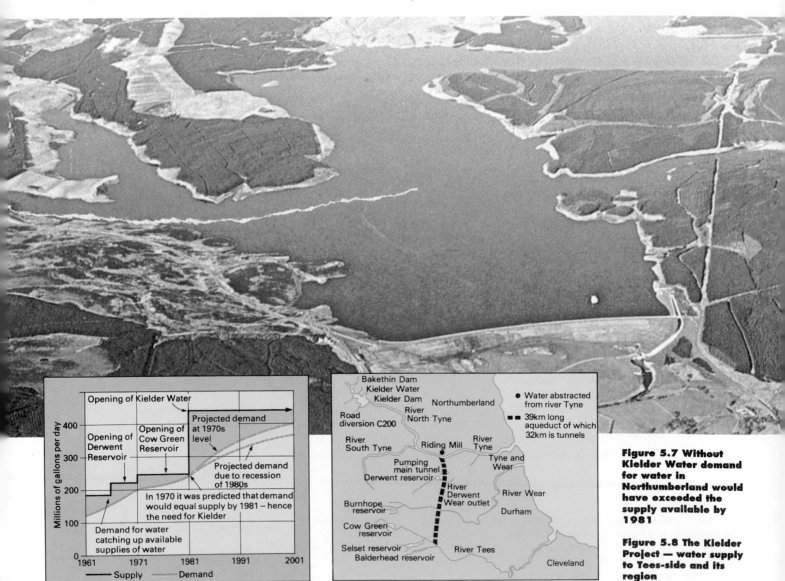

Figure 5.7 Without Kielder Water demand for water in Northumberland would have exceeded the supply available by 1981

Figure 5.8 The Kielder Project — water supply to Tees-side and its region

How does Kielder work?

Kielder Water regulates the River Tyne, from which water is taken to serve areas in the North-East. In addition to the river-regulating reservoir the scheme embodies an aqueduct to transfer water from the Tyne to the Wear and Tees, thus making Kielder supplies available to all the major urban areas of the region and, if required, to other regions as well, by pumping southwards from the Tees (Figure 5.8). No other possible scheme provided this flexibility, and any other scheme would have required five or six reservoirs to provide a yield comparable with that of Kielder. Work began in 1975, and the lake was allowed to begin to fill up in autumn 1980. By spring 1982 the reservoir was completely filled.

A multi-purpose scheme

The aim of the Kielder project was not just to provide water for the North-east of England. Unlike reservoirs built in the late eighteenth century (e.g. Thirlmere for Manchester), Kielder was planned to encourage the public to visit it and to enjoy its facilities (Figure 5.9). The development of a wide range of recreational amenities was the joint responsibility of the Forestry Commission (who planned the mainly land based activities) and the Northumbrian Water Authority (who concentrated more on water-based activities). Look carefully at Figure 5.9 and decide what provision has been made under the headings:

1 Accommodation.

2 Water sports.

3 Land-based activities.

4 Conservation attractions.

What further developments can you suggest at Kielder which might attract tourists in the 1990s?

Kielder in the 1990s

■ Two hydro-electric generators have been installed at the dam. The power produced, enough to satisfy the needs of a town of 10 000 people, is connected to the National Grid.

■ As the recession in industry led to a less rapid growth in demand for water in the North-east, the scheme has been criticised as being a 'white elephant'. Yet water supply is assured even under extreme drought conditions (Kielder was still at 90% capacity in the worst of the 1989 drought). Northumbrian Water also exports water to Gibraltar via Teesside. The authority is continually viewing opportunities for additional markets, although during the drought of 1989, Southern Water claimed it was too expensive to transport.

■ Tourism has become a major activity — indeed to the visitor it would appear that the reservoir and its surrounding Forestry Commission land has been created for recreation. Leaplish and Tower Knowe (see Figure 5.9) have become 'honeypots' i.e. areas which attract great swarms of visitors.

Figure 5.9 Recreational development at Kielder in 1989

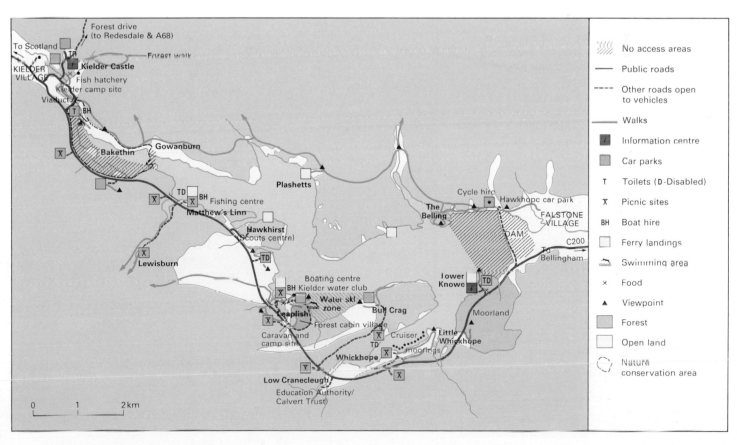

SOURCES AND PROBLEMS

Rarely a week goes by without comments on TV, radio or in the papers about Britain's energy problems — comments such as, Will we be producing too much or too little by the mid-1990s? Should we use up our coal, oil and natural gas reserves or become reliant upon nuclear power? What effect do different forms of energy have on the environment? What other forms of power could we develop by AD 2000?

Today Britain relies heavily upon four main types of energy: oil, coal, gas and nuclear energy. Look carefully at Figure 6.1 which shows the percentages of five types of energy which make up Britain's supply today, and also how these percentages have changed over the past thirty years. It must be remembered, however, that although energy consumption in Britain grew steadily since 1955 (Figure 6.2) it has recently begun to fall.

By referring to Figure 6.3 can you describe and give reasons for the present distribution of HEP (hydro-electric power) stations; nuclear power stations, coal-fired and oil-fired power stations as shown on the map? Now answer the following questions:

1 Why are the HEP stations in upland, remote areas which have heavy, reliable rainfall?

2 Why are nuclear stations usually on coastal areas, away from major cities, yet not too distant from industry?

3 Why are coal-fired stations found on or near large coalfields, near large rivers or ports, near large centres of population and industry, and with a good transport system?

4 Why are oil-fired stations found near oil refineries on coasts with deep harbours, often a long way from centres of industry and population, and often on large areas of reclaimed land?

	1950	1959	1969	1975	1983	1986	Predicted 2000 AD
Coal	90.4	76.5	50.7	36.4	33.8	32.5	33.1
Oil	9.2	22.6	42.7	42.6	37.3	35.3	30.5
Natural Gas	0	0.1	2.7	17.3	22.7	24.4	26.2
Nuclear	0	0.2	3.3	3.3	5.5	7.3	9.2
Hydro-electric	0.4	0.6	0.6	0.4	0.7	0.5	1.0

Figures show the percentage of Britain's total energy consumption supplied by each source of energy

Figure 6.1 Britain's energy consumption

Figure 6.3 Location of Britain's main power stations

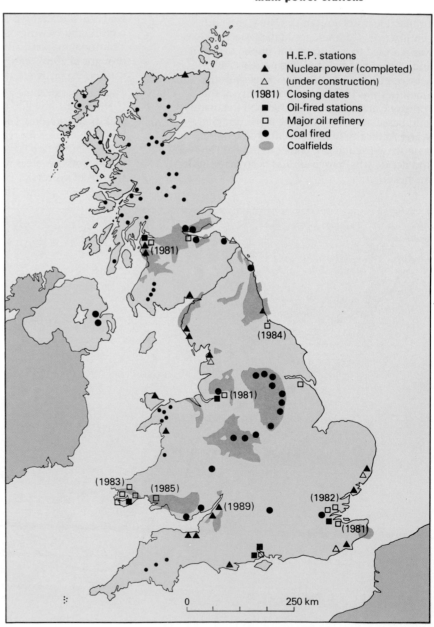

- • H.E.P. stations
- ▲ Nuclear power (completed)
- △ (under construction)
- (1981) Closing dates
- ■ Oil-fired stations
- □ Major oil refinery
- ● Coal fired
- ▨ Coalfields

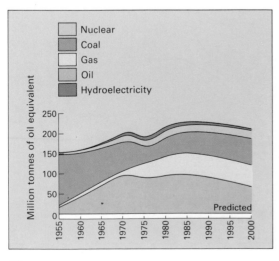

- Nuclear
- Coal
- Gas
- Oil
- Hydroelectricity

Source	Million tonnes of coal or coal equivalent
Coal	81.9
Nuclear	19.5
Oil	10.2
Natural gas	
Hydro	2.0
Electricity imports	2.7
TOTAL	116.3

Figure 6.4 Sources of electricity — power stations in the UK, 1986-7 (power station fuel consumption)

Some of the many problems and questions which must be answered in the near future are:

- Should there be a greater reliance upon coal when it remains, in 1990, our cheapest form of energy and when its reserves will last us for many years?

- Should we continue to rely so heavily on North Sea oil when its reserves may only last until AD 2020?

- Should we turn more to natural gas even if this resource may only last until AD 2050. Should we continue to use these three fossil fuels knowing that they pollute the atmosphere. The burning of coal and oil causes acid rain and together with gas, which gives off methane, contribute to the Greenhouse Effect (page 114).

- Throughout the 1980s nuclear power was considered to be both cheap and 'environmentally friendly'. Yet the Chernobyl accident in 1986 and frequent discharges of radioactive material from Sellafield into the Irish Sea have led to a growing opposition to the use of this type of energy. It was accepted, in November 1989, that the cost of electricity from nuclear power stations was twice that of electricity from coal fired stations.

- Should reliance be put upon only one major source of power? Or should supply be more balanced?

- Can conventional forms of power ensure self-sufficiency in energy supplies into the twenty-first century? Can we meet the predicted 30% growth in demand for energy between the years 1990 and 2000? How does this predicted growth in demand match the model shown in Figure 6.5?

- Should our relatively limited financial resources be spent on exploiting fossil fuels and nuclear power or on trying to develop more economic methods of using such renewable, non-pollutant forms of energy based upon the wind, waves, tide and sun?

- What will be the effects of the privatisation of the electricity industry — assuming that the scheme eventually passes through parliament?

Two views of the future (mid 1990s)

1 An industrialist's view

'We need nuclear energy quite simply because we shall be running out of oil — and of natural gas too, later on; we need coal also, as much as can be mined; and we need to do everything we can to save energy and handle it more sensibly. Nuclear, coal, conservation: those are the three legs our energy policy must stand on.

The nuclear power must make its contribution. If we build the stations at a reasonably steady rate (say one a year), we could give ourselves access to another 30 mtoc (million tonnes of oil equivalent) of primary energy from nuclear sources by the end of the century, to supplement the contributions of increased coal output and of better conservation.'

2 The view of the TUC (Trades Union Council)

'A comprehensive national energy policy, geared to ensuring sustained self-sufficiency in energy supplies without undue reliance on any one fuel, is urgently needed.

Coal output should be increased from 170 million tonnes to 200 million tonnes, by the end of the century.

The Government is urged to make a clear statement in support of limiting oil production in line with self-sufficiency.

On electricity, the TUC recommends a steady, minimum ordering programme of two gigawatts of new generating capacity a year to meet demand in the 1990s onwards. One gigawatt is equivalent to the capacity of one nuclear power station.

The TUC also calls for a further gas-cooled reactor and a continuing programme of nuclear power plants based on thermal reactors.

Gas should be confined to domestic and commercial use for small-scale water and space heating, industrial use where there is no readily available substitute, and petro-chemical needs.

Inexhaustible energy sources such as solar, wind and wave power, will have a much greater potential in the first quarter of the next century'.

Figure 6.5 Changes in the demand for energy

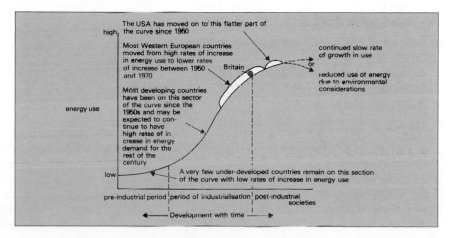

OIL AND NATURAL GAS

During the 1950s and 1960s Britain used an increasingly larger amount of oil (Figure 6.2) because:

- It was cheap to buy from Middle East countries.
- It was a clean, efficient form of energy.
- It was needed in greater quantities for Britain's expanding transport and road system.

Apart from a small oilfield in Nottinghamshire, virtually all of the gas and oil had to be imported into Britain. With the knowledge that under the North Sea were oil and natural gas-bearing rocks, exploration began off the coast of East Anglia. Natural gas was discovered in 1965 and oil in 1970 (Figure 6.6). The largest gasfield is now the Leman Bank, and the three main oilfields are the Forties, Brent and Ninian (Figure 6.6).

The problems of developing North Sea oil and gas fields

- The depth of the North Sea varies between 80 to 180 metres causing difficulties in exploring, and later exploiting, the two fuels. A new technology had to be developed before exploration could begin.
- The uneven sea bed made pipe-laying difficult.
- The high costs of constructing and maintaining oil rigs, pipelines, and storage tanks.
- The severe storms and icy Arctic winds which have caused deaths on oil rigs, under the sea, and in supplying the rigs.
- Opposition from conservationists who feared that oil spillages would affect the fishing industry, bird life, and the fine scenery of the east coast.
- The newly developed oil and gas industries would lead to a decline in the traditional, and often poorly paid, industries such as tweed making, and fishing in the North-east of Scotland.

Advantages of the North Sea oil and gas fields

- Britain's industry and economy benefits from this much needed boost.
- Reliance upon imported Middle East oil is reduced.
- It is a high quality oil.
- For a few years, Britain will become self-sufficient in oil — with even a surplus for export (Figure 6.7) to the nearby industrial countries of Europe.
- Creation of work in areas traditionally noted for **1** high unemployment and **2** depopulation (e.g. Teesside, Clydeside, eastern Scotland and the Shetlands).

- For every job created on the rigs, three or four more are needed on land, such as constructing the rigs, in supplying them, and in building new oil and gas terminals.
- Natural gas gives twice as much energy as the same amount of coal gas.
- The energy base of Britain is widened and reliance upon one fuel, which could be used as a political weapon, is reduced.

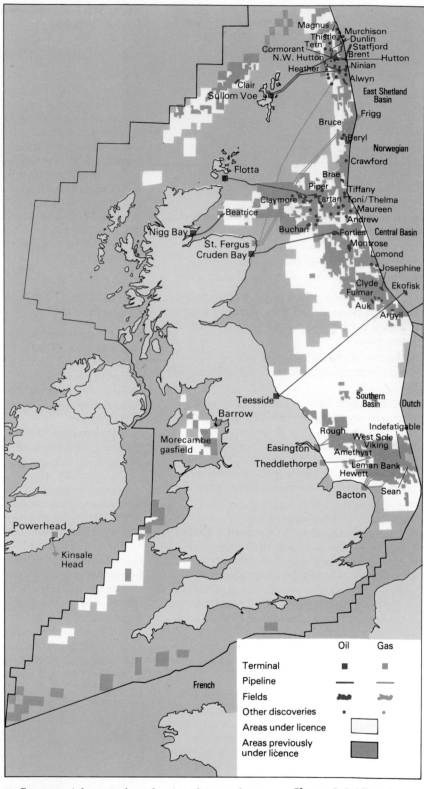

Figure 6.6 Oil and gas fields in the North Sea

The future

- Should full use be made now of oil and natural gas or should we conserve stocks so that they might last longer (Figure 6.7)?

- As Britain's industries and transport systems are geared to oil and natural gas, what happens to them when these fuels run out?

- Oil is no longer cheap, and demand is beginning to decline. Does this mean future money will be invested in other forms of power?

- Demand has fallen since 1980 (more efficient cars, less industry, alternative forms of heating) resulting in less oil needing to be refined. In 1980 BP refined 108 million tonnes, in 1984 only 59 million tonnes. Several refineries have been closed down (Figure 6.3). Will more follow?

- As fewer rigs and platforms are needed, and as oil reserves begin to decline, this is causing an increase in unemployment, especially in NE Scotland.

- Political decisions on how much to tax profits of oil companies may affect future exploration.

- Further explorations to the north-west and north-east of the Shetlands, and off SW Ireland are in deeper water, and are more prone to severe gales. Apart from increased costs and dangers, the new rigs have to be increasingly technologically advanced.

Piper Alpha, 6 July 1988

'The sea was calm and the wind light as dusk fell over the North Sea. The day shift on Occidental Petroleum's Piper Alpha oil rig, 200 km east of Wick (Figure 6.8), had just come off duty and were relaxing in their quarters two floors above the huge compressors which pressurised gas for shipment. At 21.31 these let out a high-pitched scream. There was no time to act. Within seconds a mighty explosion ripped the 220 m tall rig from top to base, engulfing it in smoke and flames which could be seen 100 km away (Figure 6.9). In the worst accident in the world's most dangerous oil-fields 170 workers lost their lives, including two of the rescuers. 64 survivors were picked up by the helicopters and ships which sped to the site. Red Adair, the American expert in tackling oil-rig disasters, was called in to help extinguish the flames'.

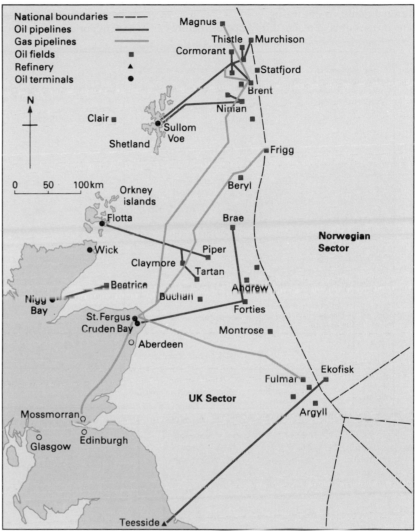

Figure 6.8 Oil and gas collecting pipelines in the North Sea

Figure 6.9 The Piper Alpha disaster, July 1988

Figure 6.7 Production forecasts for North Sea Oil

41

○ COAL

It was the development of Britain's coalfields which led to the Industrial Revolution and the growth of traditional heavy industries such as textiles, steel, shipbuilding, and engineering. Figure 6.10 shows the geology of the Yorkshire, Derby and Nottingham coalfield together with the traditional methods of mining.

The output of coal reached its peak just before the First World War (1914-18), and since then the number of miners, collieries and the total output has fallen. But significantly the amount of coal produced by each miner has increased. These changes can be seen in the data given in Figure 6.11. Figure 6.12 shows the location of the major coalfields within the National Coal Board areas, Figure 6.13 the relative and changing importance of these coalfields. Figures 6.14 and 6.15 show modern conditions above and under the ground.

Figure 6.10 Cross section of the Yorkshire, Derby and Nottingham coalfield

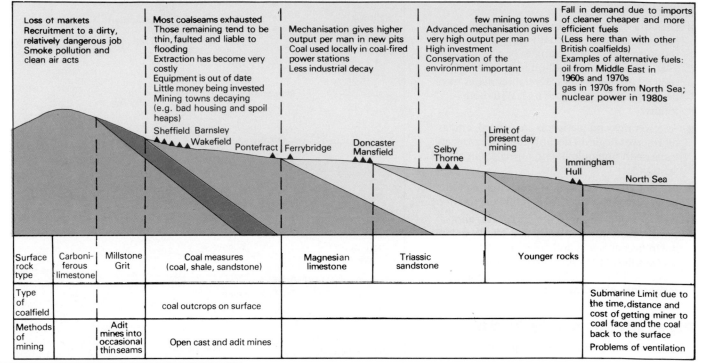

| Loss of markets Recruitment to a dirty, relatively dangerous job Smoke pollution and clean air acts | Most coalseams exhausted Those remaining tend to be thin, faulted and liable to flooding Extraction has become very costly Equipment is out of date Little money being invested Mining towns decaying (e.g. bad housing and spoil heaps) | Mechanisation gives higher output per man in new pits Coal used locally in coal-fired power stations Less industrial decay | few mining towns Advanced mechanisation gives very high output per man High investment Conservation of the environment important | Fall in demand due to imports of cleaner cheaper and more efficient fuels (Less here than with other British coalfields) Examples of alternative fuels: oil from Middle East in 1960s and 1970s gas in 1970s from North Sea; nuclear power in 1980s |

Sheffield Barnsley Wakefield — Pontefract | Ferrybridge — Doncaster Mansfield — Selby Thorne — Limit of present day mining — Immingham Hull — North Sea

Surface rock type	Carboniferous limestone	Millstone Grit	Coal measures (coal, shale, sandstone)	Magnesian limestone	Triassic sandstone	Younger rocks	
Type of coalfield			coal outcrops on surface				Submarine Limit due to the time, distance and cost of getting miner to coal face and the coal back to the surface Problems of ventilation
Methods of mining		Adit mines into occasional thin seams	Open cast and adit mines				

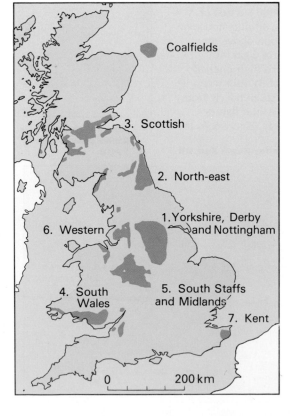

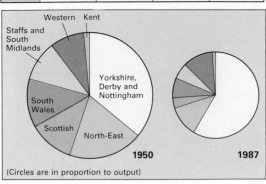

	Output (deep-mined) (million tonnes)	Active collieries	Man-power (000s)	Output per man-year (tonnes)
1950	206	901	691	298
1955	211	850	699	302
1960	187	698	602	310
1965	177	483	456	387
1970	135	292	287	470
1975	117	246	246	473
1980	109	211	233	476
1987	88	110	110	698

(Circles are in proportion to output)

Western Kent
Staffs and South Midlands
Yorkshire, Derby and Nottingham
South Wales
Scottish
North-East
1950   **1987**

Coalfields

3. Scottish
2. North-east
1. Yorkshire, Derby and Nottingham
6. Western
4. South Wales
5. South Staffs and Midlands
7. Kent

0   200 km

Figure 6.11 Coal production in the UK since 1950 (far left, above)

Figure 6.12 Location of major coalfields (left)

Figure 6.13 Coal output from the major coalfields (far left, below)

Will coal become Britain's major source of energy in the 1990s?

For

- As gas and oil reserves are depleted they will become more expensive as they get scarcer and available only from more distant fields. Coal is likely to remain the cheapest form of energy.
- Oil production can be interrupted by political unrest.
- Britain's coal reserves, based on present mining techniques and production, will last for at least another 300 years. It was accepted (in 1989) that it was our cheapest source of energy.
- Vast new reserves have recently been found in the Vale of Belvoir and North Oxfordshire as well as the Selby district of Yorkshire. In the latter, one year's production equals one twelfth of the total annual production of 1980.
- Increasing demand for coal as a source of electricity and space heating. Coal accounts for 80% of electricity generated from power stations (Figure 6.16).
- An experimental scheme at Grimthorp allows coal of all grades plus refuse collected from urban areas to be burnt on a bed of ash or sand. Air is blown through at high speed turning the coal and rubbish into a fluid. This is known as the Fluidized Bed technique.
- The oil-from-coal plant at Point of Ayr Colliery (near Flint) was seen as the forerunner to a commercial plant to produce petrol, diesel and aviation fuels from coal.

Against

- Closed pits can rarely be re-opened.
- New coalmines and coalfields are very expensive to build and develop.
- A fall in demand for energy in the early 1980s meant coal was stockpiled. It was the NCB's decision to reduce output (to match the falling demand) that helped to spark off the 1984 miners' strike.
- A return to coal means an increase in carbon dioxide to add to the Greenhouse Effect, (page 114) and acid rain.
- Increased wage demands by miners could make coal and certain mines uneconomical to mine.
- A strong nuclear energy group who favour the use of nuclear power.
- As developments in the coal industry concentrate more in the Yorkshire and Nottingham areas, traditional mining areas such as Scotland, Northumberland, Durham and South Wales will decline even more (Figure 6.13).

Figure 6.16 Main uses of coal, 1947 and 1987

Figure 6.14 A modern colliery (Stillingfleet) showing the pithead

Figure 6.15 Underground with the latest coal-cutting machinery at Ollerton colliery, Nottinghamshire

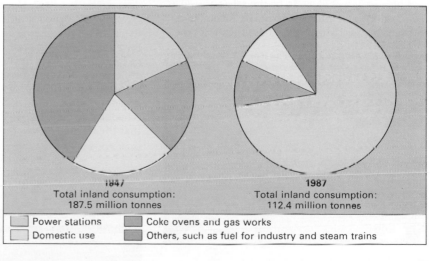

1947	1987
Total inland consumption: 187.5 million tonnes	Total inland consumption: 112.4 million tonnes

☐ Power stations ☐ Coke ovens and gas works
☐ Domestic use ☐ Others, such as fuel for industry and steam trains

NUCLEAR AND HYDRO-ELECTRIC POWER

In 1955 the British Government announced the first stage of a programme based upon nuclear power, and on improved versions of the Calder Hall (Cumbria), and Chapelcross prototypes.

Stage 1 Nine twin-reactor stations of the Magnox type (Figure 6.17) were built. Their locations (shown on Figure 6.18) were:

- Away from populated areas in case of accidents.
- Away from areas with alternative energy supplies.
- Usually on coasts, since vast amounts of water were needed for cooling purposes (Trawsfynydd, the exception, was located beside a lake Figure 6.17).
- On strong geological foundations to stand the heavy weight of the station.
- In areas with large amounts of flat land (preferably low-value farm land) for the original station and, as has frequently happened, an adjacent second station.

Stage 2 This was announced in 1964 and included the building of five improved and more economical advanced gas-cooled reactors (AGR) based upon the Windscale prototype (Figure 6.19).

Stage 3 This was announced in the late 1970s with plans for **a** two further AGR stations (at Hartlepool and Torness) and **b** several PWR (pressurised water reactors). (Both types are thermal reactors but the AGR is gas cooled and the PWR is water cooled.) Meanwhile at Dounreay a third entirely different type of reactor — the fast reactor — was being developed. This can use uranium fifty times more efficiently than either the AGR or the PWR. Plans to develop a fourth type of reactor, the SGHWR (steam generating heavy water reactor) based on the Winfrith prototype, were abandoned.

The 1980s were spent trying to decide which type of reactor was likely to be the safest as well as the most efficient and cost-effective. Although it was agreed, as early as 1982, to use the PWR type

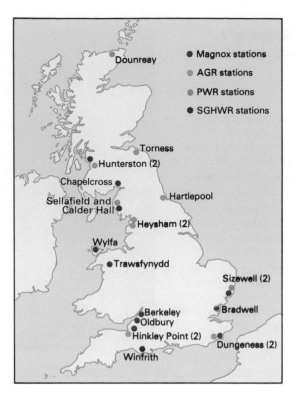

Figure 6.18 Location of nuclear power stations in Britain

Figure 6.19 Nuclear power stations — types of reactor and dates of commissioning

Magnox stations	Date commissioned	AGR stations	Date commissioned
Calder Hall*	1956	Sellafield	1962
Chapelcross	1958	Hinkley Point 'B'	1976
Berkeley	1962*	Hunterston 'B'	1976
Bradwell	1962	Dungeness 'B'	1982
Dungeness 'A'	1965	Hartlepool	1982
Hinkley Point 'A'	1965	Heysham 'A'	1982
Hunterston 'A'	1964	Heysham 'B'	1986
Oldbury on Severn	1967	Torness	1989
Sizewell 'A'	1966	**P W R stations**	
Trawsfynydd	1965	Dounreay*	1975
Wylfa	1971	Sizewell 'B'	1994
		S G H W R stations	
*prototypes		Winfrith*	1967
*closed	1989		

and that the first site would be Sizewell B, a protracted public enquiry meant that the station is not scheduled to open until 1994. By the late 1980s four PWR reactors were planned in order to meet the expected 30% increase in electricity demand by AD 2000. However in late 1989 the Government, when running into difficulties over its privatisation scheme, announced that Sizewell B was likely to be the last nuclear power station to be built. Meanwhile the original Magnox station, at Berkeley, had closed and was being 'decommissioned', a process likely to take several decades. Although other older stations are scheduled to close in the 1990s, it seems unlikely that the nuclear debate is over.

Figure 6.17 Magnox type reactor - Trawsfynydd nuclear power station, Gwynedd

Figure 6.20 The Wylfa nuclear power station, Anglesey, Gwynedd

The nuclear energy debate

For

- Several independent experts predict that without nuclear power, Britain will face an energy gap by AD 2000, and that this would mean fewer jobs and a lower standard of living. Demand for electricity is predicted to increase by 30% between 1990 and 2000 AD.

- Despite the high costs of building nuclear stations, the resultant power was the cheapest form available. In 1980 the charge was 1.32p per unit compared with the cheapest coal-fired at 1.51p. The 1987 figures were 3.6p and 2.9p. It is more efficient than rival sources of energy.

- Only very limited raw materials would be needed e.g. 50 tonnes of uranium per year compared with 540 tonnes of coal per hour needed for coal-fired stations. The proposed fast reactor uses depleted uranium — the unusable fraction after fuel has been used in Magnox, AGRs, etc. and Britain already has 20 000 tonnes in stock — the energy equivalent of 40 000 million tonnes of coal.

- Oil and natural gas could become exhausted by AD 2020. Coal is difficult to obtain and dirty to use.

- Numerous safeguards make the risks of any accident minimal.

- Nuclear waste is limited in amount and can be stored underground.

- Nearly all the money spent in Britain on energy research has been on nuclear power.

- Nuclear energy schemes have the support of large firms and government departments.

- Believed to contribute less, if at all, to the Greenhouse Effect and acid rain.

Against

- How safe is it? So far, there have been no serious accidents in Britain, as at Chernobyl, but there have been several leaks at Sellafield.

- A large conservationist lobby who claim one accident may kill many and ruin an area of ground for hundreds of years. The Irish Sea is increasingly contaminated.

- Many people think that Britain should concentrate on using renewable forms of energy rather than those that are non-renewable.

- Energy produced from raw materials found in Britain should be preferred to relying on imports from overseas.

- In November 1989 it was announced that the cost of electricity from nuclear power stations was twice that from coal-fired stations 7.0p compared to 2.9p.

- Nuclear power cannot be used for two of industry's major demands: **a** space heating and **b** transport, as costs would be too high.

- There is less demand for energy by industries because the declining industries (e.g. steel) use more energy than do the replacement industries (e.g. micro-electronics).

- Health risks: the high incidence of leukemia around Sellafield and Dounreay is being linked to the proximity of the power station.

- Nuclear waste can remain radioactive for many years. There are problems of reprocessing and then storing nuclear waste (page 118).

- Cost of decommisioning old power stations, the first of which, at Berkeley, closed in 1989.

Hydro-Electric Power

This is the most attractive form of energy as it uses a renewable source-water, it is clean and, once the station has been built, it is cheap to produce. However HEP needs:

- Heavy, reliable rainfall.
- An even run-off of surplus water.
- Steep gradients to provide a good 'head' of water.
- Lakes or reservoirs to store water so as to regulate the flow to the turbines in the power station.
- Large drainage basins to trap sufficient water.
- Steep-sided valleys for dams to be built.

Unfortunately, in Britain, such conditions are either rare or are in areas remote from where the power is needed (Figure 6.3). Just one coal-fired power station in the Trent Valley can produce more electricity than all of the HEP stations in the Scottish Highlands put together.

The Dinorwic pumped storage scheme (Snowdonia)

During the day, water from the Machlyn Mawr reservoir is allowed to fall onto turbines. The electricity produced is fed into the National Grid during peak times. At night, taking advantage of cheap off-peak electricity, the water is pumped back up into Machlyn Mawr ready for re-use the next day. If there is a breakdown in a conventional power station, the Dinorwic scheme can reach full capacity within ten seconds (Figure 6.21).

Figure 6.21 The Dinorwic Pumped Storage Scheme, Gwynedd

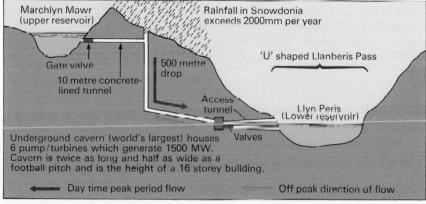

Marchlyn Mawr (upper reservoir)

Rainfall in Snowdonia exceeds 2000mm per year

Gate valve

10 metre concrete-lined tunnel

500 metre drop

'U' shaped Llanberis Pass

Access tunnel

Valves

Llyn Peris (Lower reservoir)

Underground cavern (world's largest) houses 6 pump/turbines which generate 1500 MW. Cavern is twice as long and half as wide as a football pitch and is the height of a 16 storey building.

← Day time peak period flow   Off peak direction of flow →

RENEWABLE RESOURCES

As we have seen earlier, (Figure 6.1) the major sources of energy in Britain are non-renewable fuels. Advocates of each of these types of energy tend to dismiss new potential sources of power.

The following extract is from an information booklet issued by the United Kingdom Atomic Energy Authority.

'Nuclear energy is in a different category from the 'renewable' sources of energy like the sun, wind, waves and tides. These are at a very early stage of development and could not offer relief on a large scale before the end of this century. They have to overcome the problems of their dependence upon the weather and the need for their production structures in some cases to be strong enough to stand up to a wide range of stresses brought about by strong winds and stormy seas, without becoming too expensive to build. Research and development are being actively pursued and these energy sources may well be very valuable in the more distant future. However, it would be a grave mistake to rely on them to make a major contribution to our energy problem in sufficient time.'

Amongst the arguments put forward in the above extract against solar, wind, tidal, wave and biogas power are:

■ Research is still in an early stage of development.

■ These sources of power are unlikely to be able to produce energy until well into the twenty-first century.

■ Vast sums of money are needed for research and development.

■ At present renewable resources are more expensive to produce than traditional fuels.

■ Such forms of power would have to depend upon Britain's unreliable weather.

But, as present forms of energy become more expensive and increasingly pollute the environment, should not longer-term alternatives be considered?

Solar energy

The sun gives the earth 100 000 times as much energy as we need. Although solar power is being exploited in several parts of the world, it will continue to have a high cost method of conversion until new technology can bring down those costs and the surplus can be stored (essential in a cloudy Britain). Even by AD 2000 solar energy is expected to provide less than 1% of Britain's needs.

Methods of harnessing solar power

■ **Solar collectors**. These are glass-covered panels allowing sunlight to pass through the glass and to be trapped inside a box-like apparatus (Figure 6.22).

Figure 6.22 Solar heating

■ **Solar farms**. These are huge reflectors, laid out on an open space. They concentrate sunlight into pipes containing gases which then become heated to high temperatures.

■ **Photovoltaic cells**. These were initially used in space exploration, and can produce electricity.

Wind power

To be at their most efficient, wind turbines need to be in areas with high and regular wind speeds. The first turbine was built at Carmarthen Bay (South Wales) in 1982 and enlarged in 1987. A second turbine, in use by 1983, was at Burgar Hill in the Orkneys where the average annual wind speed is 50 km. This giant 'windmill' is as tall as Nelson's Column. Since then smaller turbines have been built at Richborough (Kent), Ilfracombe (Devon) and Machynlleth (Dyfed). Although wind turbines are more environmentally acceptible than conventional forms of energy in that they are safe and do not pollute the atmosphere, they can interfere with local radio and television reception and are noisy and unsightly — it takes 7000 individual turbines to produce the same electricity as one nuclear power station! Economically, as

Figure 6.23 A proposed wind farm, Burgar Hill, Orkneys

turbines are expensive to build and to maintain, it is an advantage to develop many small machines grouped together to form a 'wind farm'. Three proposed sites are at Cold Northcott (Cornwall), Capel Cynon (Dyfed) and Langdon Common (Durham). A typical 'farm' would have 25 turbines in an area of 3 km² (Figure 6.23). The proposed site of the world's first offshore turbine is 5 km north of Wells (Norfolk). Wind power could provide five percent of Britain's energy by AD 2000.

Biogas energy

This consists mainly of methane and carbon dioxide which can be obtained from plants or crop wastes. The Scottish Highlands and Islands Development Board are researching into the possibilities of this energy with the help of an EC grant.

Tides and tidal barrages

The incoming tide also contains much potential energy, especially in several estuaries on the West coast which have a high tidal range. If the tide were to pass through sluices in a barrage, and after being held behind this 'dam' could be released back into the sea, it is estimated that this method could provide 15% of Britain's present needs. Over the years similar ideas have been linked to the Solway, Morecambe Bay, the Dee and the Severn Estuary. Such a scheme drawn up for the Severn Estuary is shown in Figure 6.24. The British Government now has to determine whether a full feasibility study of this scheme should be set up to study the type and size of barrage, and its social and environmental impact. This study could take four years, and if acceptable, it would take a further nine years to complete the scheme. The cost to the consumer of electricity produced by this method is becoming more attractive as costs from other energy sources are only slightly less expensive.

Wave power

Estimates concerning the potential energy produced by waves around Britain predict that this method could meet 20-33% of Britain's energy needs i.e. all Britain's extra demands by 2000 AD. The problem is in designing machinery capable of withstanding the power of storm waves. Yet waves are a renewable source, and most storms occur in the winter which is the time of peak energy demand. Research is still in its infancy, but, if applied, wave machines such as the one in Figure 6.25 could be constructed off North-east Scotland, North-west Scotland and Lands End. A wave generator of about 1MW capacity is planned for experiments on the sea bed off Lewis (Hebrides).

Return now to the questions on page 39 and decide how you would try to solve Britain's energy problems for the year AD 2000.

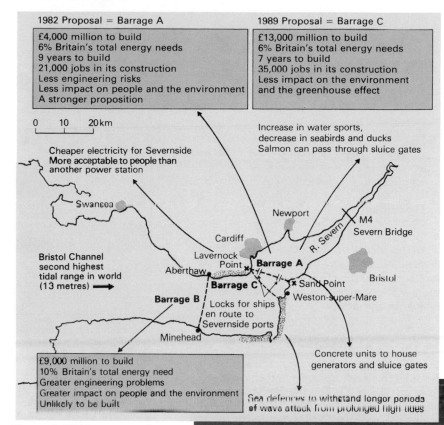

Figure 6.24 The proposed Severn Tidal barrage

Figure 6.25 Prototype wave-powered electricity generator, Islay, Scotland. This device will eventually be used to supply electricity to small, isolated communities

Hot water test drill a success

BRITAIN'S first attempt to tap a reservoir of hot water deep down in the earth's crust to use as an energy source has proved a success, the Junior Energy Minister, Mr John Moore, announced yesterday.

The £1.8 million well, at Marchwood, near Southampton, found water at 5,500ft.

Allowing for heat loss in transit, the water will come to the surface at a temperature of 65-67 degrees centigrade. There is sufficient to heat about 1,000 homes for several decades. Further wells of similar potential could be drilled into the same reservoir.

The use of geothermal heat—water heated by "hot rocks" in the earth's crust—is new technology in Britain, although systems of this kind have been operational in Europe for some time.

"Although its uses are limited by the amount of geothermal water in Britain's rock structure, this new resource might eventually prove a useful alternative to conventional fuels in heating homes and offices," Mr Moore told MPs.

Further tests are to continue in Cornwall.

Figure 6.26 Geothermal heat — Britain's first attempt

○ THE FACTORY AS A SYSTEM

Industry as a whole, or a factory as an individual unit, can be regarded as a system. This system can be represented in the following way:

Inputs	→	Factory	→	Outputs
(raw materials and human inputs) Expenditure		(manufacturing processes)		(end products) Income

In this model, outputs (income) minus inputs (expenditure) will give that industry or firm a profit or a loss. For a firm to remain profitable, some of the income must be re-invested to modernise the factory.

Industrial location

Before building a factory, the manufacturer should consider the major elements in the system diagram (Figure 7.1). It is unlikely that the manufacturer will find all the elements operating at one site, and so a decision must be made as to which site has the greatest advantages.

For the older established British industries, their location was often determined by physical conditions, but today other factors tend to be more important. Where many sites are available, the firm or company will choose the most profitable one. This will be the site where the costs of raw materials, fuel and power, labour, land and transport are minimised, and where there is a large market for the product. These factors are summarised in Figure 7.1 where they have been divided into **a** physical factors and **b** human and economic factors.

In the late twentieth century the three major

Figure 7.1 Factors affecting the location of industry

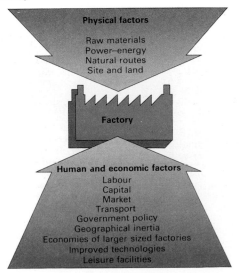

factors deciding industrial location are possibly the nearness to a large market, the availability of labour and government policy. In the nineteenth century it was such physical factors as the source of raw materials (e.g. iron ore) and sources of energy (e.g. coal) which determined industrial locations. Figure 7.2 shows the major areas of traditional heavy industry in Britain. Now study the maps in Figure 7.3 together with Figure 7.1 and list the reasons for the growth of:

1 Steel at:
   a Sheffield,
   b Scunthorpe,
   c Port Talbot.
2 Car assembly plants in Coventry and Birmingham.

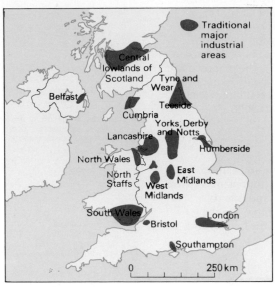

Figure 7.2 The traditional industrial areas

Figure 7.3 Location of a) integrated iron and steel works, b) motor vehicle assembly plants

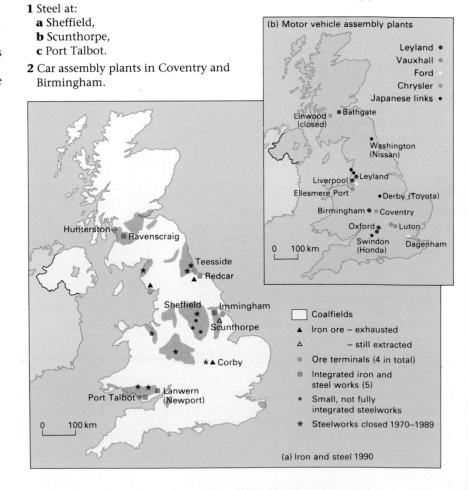

48

Industry today

The reasons which led to the growth and location of those heavy industries (Figure 7.3) in the nineteenth century are, however, mainly irrelevant today. The problems of the 1990s are how and where to create new jobs, rather than the location of steelworks, shipyards and textile mills built over a hundred years ago. Yet industrial decline was not new to the 1980s; coalmines, for example, have been closing in parts of North-east England, South Wales and Central Scotland since the 1930s; textile mills since the 1960s; shipyards since the 1970s and steelworks and car assembly plants in the 1980s. The numbers employed in the textile industry reveal this trend. In 1955 it employed 282 000; 1965, 159 000; 1975, 79 000 and in 1986, 24 000. Figure 7.4 shows the economic planning regions in Britain and Figure 7.5 the steady rise in unemployment after 1972, the rapid rise of the early 1980s and steady decline after 1985.

1 Rank the 11 regions given in Figure 7.5 in order of unemployment for 1972 (highest = 1; lowest = 11).

a What do you notice about the location of the four regions with the highest unemployment? How do you account for this?

b What do you notice about the location of the four regions with lowest unemployment? How do you account for this? (Refer to Figure 7.8 for help in answering these questions).

2 Using Figure 7.6, how do you account for the high rate of unemployment in mid 1985?

3 Rank the 11 regions again using the 1990 figures. Describe any changes in the rank order between 1990 and 1972. Some of the reasons for the decline in unemployment after 1985 are given on pages 54-57.

Region	1972	1977	Mid 1985	Jan 1990
\multicolumn{5}{l}{Registered unemployed in the UK as a % total number of employees}
Northern	6.9	9.3	18.5	9.0
Yorks and Humberside	4.8	6.5	14.6	7.1
North West	5.0	8.3	15.9	7.9
East Midlands	3.6	5.7	12.4	5.2
West Midlands	5.0	6.6	15.1	6.1
East Anglia	3.6	5.7	10.3	3.7
South East	2.4	5.0	9.6	3.8
South West	4.2	7.3	11.3	4.5
Wales	5.8	9.0	16.3	7.2
Scotland	7.1	8.7	15.3	8.8
Northern Ireland	8.9	12.6	20.9	14.2

Figure 7.5 Changes in regional unemployment

Causes of job losses and industrial decline

Figure 7.6 lists some of the causes of job losses. Until recently the loss of jobs in one area (e.g. North-east England) meant a gain in jobs in another area (e.g. South-east England).The 1980s showed that:

■ If one big company closes, it leads to job losses in associated firms.

■ Most unemployment is in old inner city areas.

■ Most unemployment is in the regions furthest from London.

■ When a large steelworks (Corby, Consett) or a car assembly plant (Linwood) closes, thousands of jobs are lost and there arises the difficulty of having to find replacement employment.

■ The danger of one area or town relying on one type of industry or one firm for employment.

■ New high-tech industries do not employ as many people as older industries.

Using Figure 7.6, choose a local firm which has closed recently and then fill in the first column giving reasons for the closure. Next, referring to pages 50 and 51 complete the columns headed Coalmining, and Steel.

Figure 7.6 Causes of unemployment and industrial decline

SOLIHULL S.F.C. LIBRARY

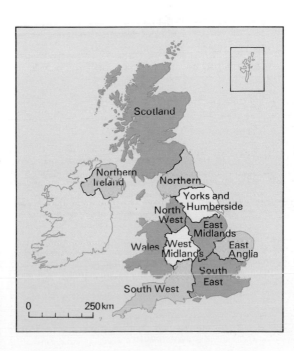

Reasons for job losses	Example from your local area	Coal mining	Steel
Exhaustion of resources			
Introduction of new machinery or new methods needing fewer workers (automation)			
Fall in demand for product			
Site needed for other uses			
Large scale redevelopment of inner city areas			
Closure due to high costs of production — high wages			
Closure due to high costs of production — old, inefficient methods or difficult condition			
Rationalisation programme of a larger company			
Competition from overseas			
Lack of money for investment			
Competition from rival products			
Political decisions which deny government financial assistance to ailing companies			

○ INDUSTRIAL DECLINE

Coalmining in South Wales

Coal production reached a peak in South Wales in 1913 when 50 million tonnes were produced, but since then output has continually declined until it was only 6$\frac{1}{2}$ million tonnes in 1987-88. In the early 1920s one man in three was employed in the coal industry. In 1989 it was only one in a hundred. When the industry was nationalised in 1945 there were 214 pits in South Wales. At the beginning of 1990 there were only six.

Figure 7.7 shows closures in the Neath Valley since 1914.

The most easily obtainable coal has long since been recovered, and many of the remaining seams are narrow and faulted making them difficult and dangerous to work. Many of the older collieries suffer from out-dated machinery, and like other nationalised industries, there has been a lack of heavy investment for the future. Indeed, successive governments have preferred to spend money on developing alternative forms of energy such as oil and nuclear power which tend to be both cheaper and often more efficient. Yet even the newer collieries, especially those producing anthracite (Figure 7.8), only tend to add to the loss in jobs as automation and modern machinery replace human labour. Although coalminers may still not be so well paid as some other workers, they have pushed up the price of coal by their wage increases, and this has led to a loss in the traditional export trade as foreign countries can now buy cheaper coal from the USA. Even within Britain, the South Wales collieries are less economical and located further from domestic markets than the newer collieries in Yorkshire and the East Midlands.

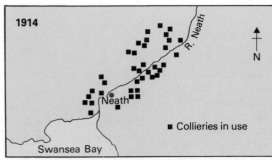

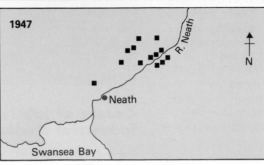

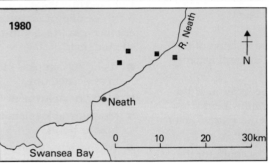

Figure 7.7 Colliery closures in the Neath valley, West Glamorgan

Figure 7.9 Employment figures for Corby, Northampton

Year	Total population	Total employees	Steel workers	% working in steel
1934	1500	500	0	0
1956	24 000	14 423	9959	69
1966	43 900	24 071	12 982	54
1976	52 000	24 623 (Closed down)	12 227	50
1981	52 667	24 560	6200	27
1985	**53 212**	**23 876**	**2320**	**9.5**

Figure 7.8 The increase in job losses and unemployment has been, throughout this century, much greater in the north and west than in the south and east

The North and West

The exhaustion of raw materials (coal, iron ore)

The decline in the 'heavy' manufacturing industry (steel, ships, textiles and engineering)

The greater distance and remoteness from the largest market (London) and the EC

The recession hitting manual workers more than non-manual, with the North having had the majority of the manual jobs

A greater loss of jobs in the older industries which tended to be located in inner city areas of conurbations — and most conurbations are in the North and west

MIGRATION FOR JOBS

The South and East

London, being the capital, has job opportunities in government (administration) and in offices (there is prestige value in locating a firm's headquarters in the capital city). It is the centre of commerce

Having the largest market, the area has most service industries (e.g. shops, schools, hospitals)

The more rural counties surrounding London never had large numbers in the secondary sector and so have been less affected by the recession

Larger numbers are employed in tourism — a growth industry

Steel making in Corby

In 1934 Corby was a small village situated on a vast iron-ore field when Stewarts & Lloyds decided to convert the ore found on the spot into steel, and then the steel into tubes in one continuous process. The demand for a large workforce led to many families coming from Scotland (57% of the present population originated from Scotland), but as the industry developed, Corby became virtually a one industry town (Figure 7.9).

In 1980 the British Steel Corporation (BSC) had to close down the steel making side at Corby. This was because the strip which it produced was so expensive that the tube works found it impossible to compete on the world markets. When the steelworks closed, Corby had only 63 jobs on offer, of which 55 were skilled. This meant that a largely unskilled workforce had either to move, commute or join the dole queue.

Following the closure, the tube Works obtained steel strip from elsewhere in BSC at a lower cost enabling it to become competitive again. Despite the rapid reduction in the numbers employed by BSC (Figure 7.9), it still remained, in 1985, the biggest single employer in Corby with a workforce of 2320.

Corby has also benefited from having been designated, in 1981, an Enterprise Zone, (page 124). Improved road links have been made with the M1 and A1, while government and EC grants and a vigorous advertising policy have encouraged new firms to locate here (e.g. Weetabix, Avon Cosmetics and Golden Wonder Crisps). Although the average workforce for each new firm is only 50 (compare with the original workforce at BSC) Corby has become a more balanced town and instead of relying on one industry to supply its employment needs it now has a wider industrial base.

British shipbuilding

Britain has fallen from being the world's leading shipbuilding nation of the inter-war years to eleventh place. Many of the building and repair yards have had to close because of:

- A decline in orders because of increased overseas competition.
- The decline following the recession in world trade.
- Competition from other forms of transport.
- A decline in the demand for naval warships over the world.

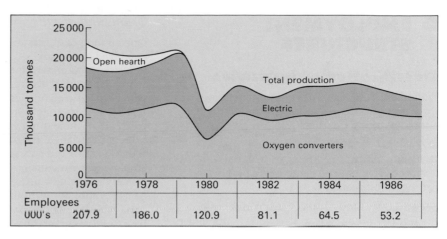

| Employees UUU's | 207.9 | 186.0 | 120.9 | 81.1 | 64.5 | 53.2 |

Figure 7.10 The decline of the steel industry in Britain

- A decline in demand for passenger ships.
- Rationalisation of British shipyards.
- Lack of investment in the nationalised industry.
- Much out-of-date equipment.
- Production costs which are higher than in many rival countries.

Figures 7.11 and 7.12 show the decline in employees and in ships launched up to 1985. Since then many of the remaining yards have become privatised and to obtain total figures would mean writing individually to each firm. By 1990 shipbuilding had virtually ceased in North-east England. The last yards on the Wear and Tees had closed, and Swan Hunters on the Tyne (apart from three frigates for the Royal Navy) had a virtually empty order book.

Figure 7.12 Decline in shipbuilding

Launching in tonnes (000s)			
	1938	1971	1985
NE England	425	568	148
Clyde	444	284	141
UK	1030	1239	456

World orders declined from 74 million tonnes in 1973 to an estimated 25 million in 1985.

Figure 7.13 A derelict shipyard

Figure 7.11 Employees in British shipbuilding

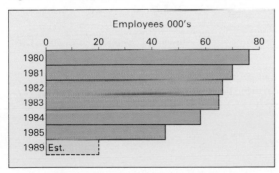

○ EMPLOYMENT STRUCTURES

Classification of industries

Traditionally, industry has been broken down into three groups (primary, secondary and tertiary), although during the 1980s a fourth group was added (quaternary).

Primary industries extract raw materials directly from the earth or sea. Examples are farming, fishing, forestry and mining.

Secondary industries process and manufacture the primary products (e.g. steelworks, shipbuilders or furniture-makers). They include the construction industry and the assembly of components made by other secondary industries.

Tertiary industries provide a service. These include health, education, office work, local and national government, retailing, entertainment and transport.

Quaternary industries provide information and expertise. The new microchip and micro-electronics industries come into this category.

Figure 7.15 shows the percentage of British workers (out of a total workforce of 25 million) employed in the three main categories, and the differences within each group between male and female employees. Describe carefully what these figures show and mean.

Figure 7.15 Changes in employment in the major sectors of industry (%)

	1961	1988	%Males 1977	%Females 1977
Primary	6	3	79	21
Secondary	46	28	82	18
Tertiary	48	69	44	56
		Total (1988)	55	45
		Total (1974)	61	39

Triangular graphs

One method of illustrating the percentages employed in primary, secondary and tertiary industries is to present these three variables on a triangular graph. This is an equilateral triangle with each 'base' divided into percentage scales to represent each variable. It may be more convenient, though not essential, to have the sides of the triangle 10 cm in length. Figure 7.16 shows how the three variables are plotted for the employment structure of Town A. The figure for primary is found by using the left hand scale (see 'green' graph), for secondary by using the right hand scale (see 'blue' graph) and for tertiary the base (see 'orange' graph). The answer for Town A is given in the table underneath the graph. Complete this table (Figure 7.16) for Towns B and C. These three towns represent, but not necessarily in this order, a small market town, a holiday resort and an industrial town. Which figures do you think fit each letter? Give reasons for your answer.

Figure 7.15 shows how Britain has declined as a manufacturing nation with the percentage of its working population in the secondary sector having declined from 46% in 1961 to 28% in 1988. Figure 7.17 illustrates how the location of the remaining secondary industry is still unevenly distributed.

1 Figure 7.17 shows the employment structures of Britain's economic regions in 1988.

a Describe and account for the distribution of primary industry

b Describe and account for the distribution of secondary industry

c Describe and account for the distribution of tertiary industry.

Figure 7.14 Classification of industry (below left)

Figure 7.16 Triangular graph showing employment structures (below)

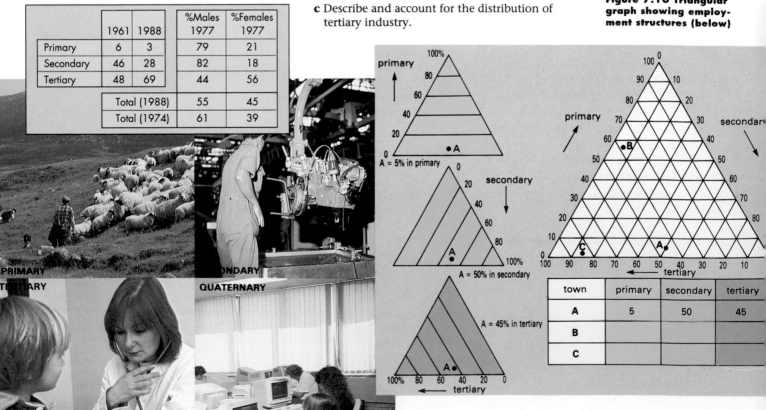

town	primary	secondary	tertiary
A	5	50	45
B			
C			

PRIMARY

SECONDARY

TERTIARY

QUATERNARY

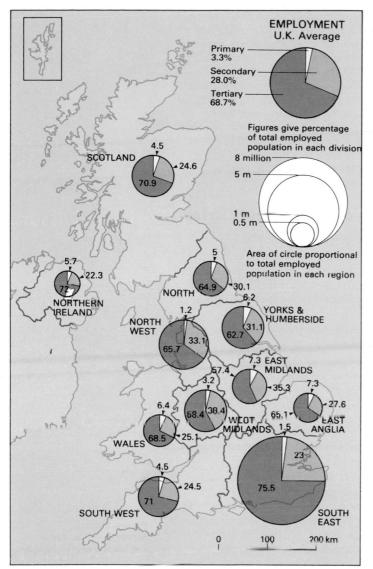

EMPLOYMENT
U.K. Average

Primary 3.3%
Secondary 28.0%
Tertiary 68.7%

Figures give percentage of total employed population in each division

8 million
5 m
1 m
0.5 m

Area of circle proportional to total employed population in each region

SCOTLAND 4.5 / 24.6 / 70.9

NORTHERN IRELAND 5.7 / 22.3 / 72

NORTH 5 / 64.9 / 30.1

NORTH WEST 1.2 / 65.7 / 33.1

YORKS & HUMBERSIDE 6.2 / 62.7 / 31.1

EAST MIDLANDS 7.3 / 57.4 / 35.3

WEST MIDLANDS 3.2 / 58.4 / 38.4

EAST ANGLIA 7.3 / 65.1 / 27.6

WALES 6.4 / 68.5 / 25.1

SOUTH WEST 4.5 / 71 / 24.5

SOUTH EAST 1.5 / 75.5 / 23

0   100   200 km

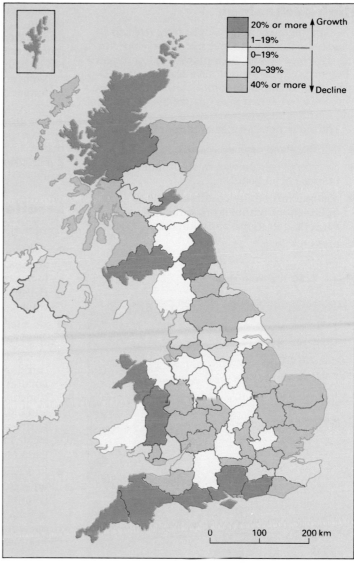

20% or more ↑ Growth
1–19%
0–19%
20–39%
40% or more ↓ Decline

0   100   200 km

2 Figure 7.18 shows the changes in manufacturing employment in the counties of Britain between 1961 and 1986.

a Describe and account for the location of those counties which have had a decrease of over 40% in manufacturing employment

b Describe and account for the location of those counties which have had an increase of over 20% in manufacturing employment.

3 Figure 7.19 shows changes in employment in selected manufacturing and service (tertiary) industries.

a Why has there been a decrease in most manufacturing industries and an increase in most service industries?

b Why have two of the selected manufacturing industries shown an increase in employment?

c Why have two of the selected service industries shown a decrease in employment?

Figure 7.17 Employment structures in Britain, (1988)

Figure 7.18 Change in manufacturing employment 1961-1986

Figure 7.19 Employment changes in selected industries, 1978-1986

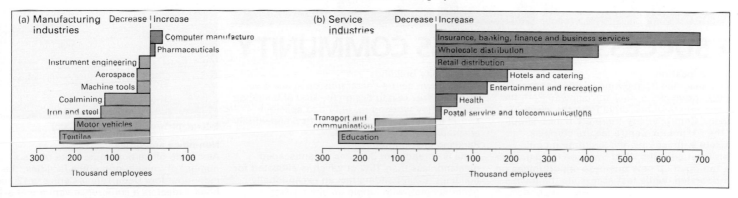

(a) Manufacturing industries   Decrease | Increase

Computer manufacture
Pharmaceuticals
Instrument engineering
Aerospace
Machine tools
Coalmining
Iron and steel
Motor vehicles
Textiles

300   200   100   0   100
Thousand employees

(b) Service industries   Decrease | Increase

Insurance, banking, finance and business services
Wholesale distribution
Retail distribution
Hotels and catering
Entertainment and recreation
Health
Postal service and telecommunications
Transport and communication
Education

300   200   100   0   100   200   300   400   500   600   700
Thousand employees

High-technology

The term high technology, or hi-tech, refers to those industries which have mainly developed in the last twenty years. Their processing techniques often involve micro-electronics and demand a high level, i.e. input, of information and expertise. They are also referred to as quaternary, (page 52) and sunrise industries.

The industries classified as hi-tech include:

- aerospace and defence systems,
- electronics (silicon wafers, semiconductors and printed circuit boards),
- communications (telecommunications, information technology, fax, financial services, bar coding in shops) and computers,
- biotechnology.

Figure 7.20 A silicon chip

The first computer marketed in 1950 cost, in present-day values, about £1 million and filled a room, whereas nowadays a micro-computer with much greater capacity, and 30 000 times smaller can be bought for just £200.

Reduction in cost and in size and an increase in performance and reliability are the factors behind the growth and impact of micro-electronics.

The growth of hi-tech industries in Britain has been very rapid — although at a rate far behind that in Japan and the USA. One reason for Britain's slower growth is the shortage of a trained, skilled workforce.

Locations of hi-tech industries

These may be summarised as follows:

- The pioneer hi-tech industries, linked to aerospace and defence systems, which still tend to be concentrated in southern England. Hertfordshire remains the county with most employees.
- On sites controlled by the Scottish (page 55) and Welsh Development Agencies.
- Along the M4 (Sunrise Strip) and M11 corridors. Sunrise Strip extends westwards from London (Heathrow airport) towards Newbury (Video Valley) Swindon, Bristol (Aztec West) and into South Wales. The M11 extends northwards from London to Cambridge. Firms locate here in attractively landscaped business parks (Figures 7.21 and 7.22).
- In Science Parks which are sited near universities and polytechnics. Indeed by definition the 62 widely located Science Parks in Britain in 1989 had to 'have formal and operational links with a higher education institute or a major centre of research'.

Figure 7.21 Advertisement for a business park — Swindon

A SUCCESSFUL BUSINESS COMMUNITY

Strategic location
Delta is one mile from Swindon town centre; five minutes' drive along dual carriageway from the M4; and two minutes' drive from the West Swindon Centre, where there are banks, shops and the £11m Link Centre leisure complex, complete with ice rink and swimming pool.

This location in the West Swindon rapid growth area can open up new business opportunities on your doorstep, while fast access via the town's excellent rail and motorway links — to London, other UK business centres, and major airports — puts domestic and foreign markets within easy reach.

High quality buildings
Lack of town-centre constraints on space gives architects free rein to design the kind of buildings people enjoy working in: light and spacious — and, at the same time, totally practical and infitely adaptable to occupiers' needs.

Parkland environment
Delta is spread over 30 acres of landscaped parkland, less than 15% of which is allocated for buildings. Each building has an exceptionally generous plot, with ample on-site parking

Intergraph headquarters (Delta 100)

Non-office amenities
Alongside office buildings, Delta offers a number of unique, non-office facilities; the indoor/outdoor Delta Tennis Centre; a 120-bed hotel — ideal as a conference venue and a shop and bank

Figure 7.22 Delta Office Park, Swindon

The micro-electronics industry in Central Scotland: 'The Silicon Glen'

By 1985 270 micro-electronic firms had moved to Central Scotland (Figure 7.23). Each of these firms has its own specialisation. For example:

- Ferranti and Marconi make defence systems.
- National Semi-Conductor, Motorola and General Instruments manufacture semi-conductors.
- Burroughs, Digital, IBM, Honeywell and NCR are connected with data processing.
- Hewlett Packard and Veeder Root deal with instrumentation.
- Rodime manufacture disc-drives (the only major Scottish-owned company).

Some of the reasons put forward by micro-electronic firms for choosing Central Scotland are:

- A tradition of electronics manufacture in the area.
- A ready availability of skilled labour.
- High productivity from the local workforce.
- A low absenteeism (7%) and better labour relations than most other areas in Britain.
- Good communications which include a modern motorway and rail network as well as ocean ports and a position near to an international airport. Neither the raw materials nor the finished product are bulky to transport.
- Financial incentives from both central government, as a result of the regions being in a Special Development area, and the Scottish Development Agency (see pages 124-5).
- There are eight local universities where 40% of graduates qualify in scientific and technological subjects. 'Science Parks' are where micro-electronic firms locate on university premises.
- A newly created Scottish Micro-electronics Applications Centre.
- New Towns, with their modern houses, factories and services, have sites available.
- Pure water for integrated circuits.

By 1985 42 000 people were employed in micro-electronics in Scotland, almost as many as in the three traditional industries of coalmining, steel and shipbuilding put together. Over 90% of the companies are from the USA (the largest number) and Japan, with the balance from the Netherlands, West Germany and, a poor last, Britain. Eleven of the top US electronic companies have a base in Scotland, although most Scottish factories are only assemblers for overseas-designed products. Yet the success of this area is continually attracting more overseas companies, and by the end of 1985 half of Britain's microchip output was estimated to have come from Scotland. Since then, the area has not kept pace with Britain's two major growth regions:

1 the M4 corridor and Hertfordshire,
2 Cambridge and the M11.

Future problems

- It is claimed that Japanese supremacy lies in cost effectiveness in production, American supremacy in entrepreneurial skill and speed, and Britain's supremacy in inventiveness. Can Britain maximise its inventiveness before being possibly overrun by American and Japanese competition?
- How quickly can Britain adapt? In 1981 only 24% of British firms claimed that they were using micro-electronics, a figure which rose to 47% by 1985 and 59% in 1989. Yet this was still lower than most industrial rivals.
- How can managers be made to appreciate the value of electronics in making their businesses more efficient and their products more attractive? In effect, a radical change is needed in work habits and attitudes from the boardroom to the factory floor.
- Will micro-electronics provide many new jobs (as appears to be the case in Scotland) or will it replace many more manual jobs?
- Does Britain have the money to fully develop micro-electronics?

Figure 7.23 Micro-electronics in Scotland—the 'Silicon Glen'

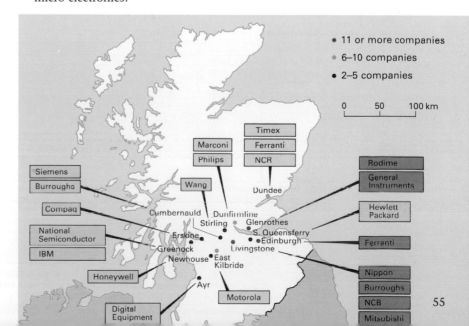

55

○ **FOOTLOOSE INDUSTRIES**

Changing industrial locations

The first two large industrial estates in Britain were at Trafford Park in Manchester (1896) and at Slough, West London (1920); both were private enterprises. Following the Depression of the 1930s, successive governments have helped to create more of these estates. At Team Valley in Gateshead (1936) a trading estate was so named because it included warehousing and distributive units as well as having small scale manufacturing firms. Figure 7.25 shows some of the differences between the traditional industrial site, and these newer industrial or trading estates.

The term 'footloose' is applied to those firms which have a relatively free choice of location. Many of these newer industries provide services for people and are therefore market orientated. The raw materials are often component goods made elsewhere, and the finished product is usually light and easily transportable by road or air.

Location

Two prime sites for these footloose industries are:

1 On large trading or industrial estates built on former greenfield sites on the edges of towns and cities (Figure 7.24).

2 Alongside major motorways to capitalise upon efficient transport links (e.g. M3 in Figure 7.24).

Advantages of an edge-of-town location
(Figure 8.15)

■ Cheaper land values away from the CBD as competition for land is lower near to the city boundary (lower rents and rates).

■ Ample space for the construction of large buildings, car parks and lorry unloading bays, together with room for possible future expansion.

Frigure 7.24 An industrial estate outside Basingstoke, Hampshire

■ Well planned, modern estates, often with local roads, services and factory units built in advance.

■ A good internal road system linked by main roads to motorway intersections.

Layout of estates

■ Roads are usually wide and straight, or gently curving, to allow easy access and turning for large delivery lorries.

■ Each factory unit is in its own relatively large area of land with room for expansion, and its own car and lorry park.

■ Some vacant sites have been designated to try to attract firms in future years.

■ Adjacent to modern, suburban housing estates, both private and council, as well as access to commuter villages which provide a local labour force — an increasing proportion of which is female.

■ A pleasant working environment, as these new industries provide very little air or noise pollution.

■ Access to urban markets.

Figure 7.25 Changing industrial locations

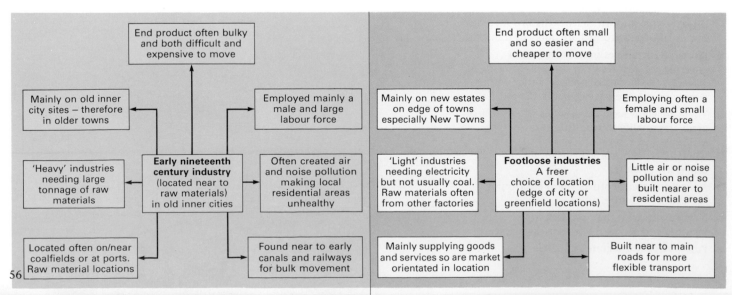

Types of firm

- Distributive firms which can warehouse their goods either for dispatch by motorways to other parts of the country or for later delivery to the CBD (e.g. food, drink, car parts) (Figure 7.26).
- Food processing firms.
- Light, small scale, manufacturing industries.
- Hi-tech firms.
- The more recent addition of offices, hotels and hypermarkets .

The demand for leisure and social activities is now an important consideration in locating new firms.

Multi or transnational companies (TNCs)

A multinational company, usually now called a transnational company, is one which operates in many countries, regardless of national frontiers. The headquarters are usually in developed countries with, increasingly, the 'branch' factories in developing countries. Multinational companies directly employ about 30 million people around the world, and indirectly influence an even larger number. Many companies have annual sales larger than the GNP of some European countries. The largest 100 firms (led by oil companies and car firms) controlled one-fifth of the world's manufacturing output in 1965, and one-third by 1985. The four largest ones had, in 1985, a bigger turnover than all of Africa's GNP.

Japanese car firms in Britain

When Japanese imports, including cars, began to flood the western markets in the late 1970s and early 1980s, steps were made to try to control this one-way trade.

Countries such as the UK negotiated voluntary agreements with Japan to the effect that, for example, the volume of Japanese cars imported into Britain would not exceed 11% of Britain's passenger car market. Following this, Japanese car manufacturers began to look for ways to overcome this barrier, and to produce cars within Britain.

When, in 1981, the British government decided to allow Nissan to build a factory to assemble cars, several areas with high unemployment began a highly active campaign to attract the company. The former Tyne and Wear council successfully lobbied the Japanese by showing that Nissan could get grants to cover one-third of their building costs by being in a development area, that a huge area of flat land (formerly Sunderland airport) was already available, that the site was adjacent to the A1(M), near to the Tyne, Wear and Tees for the import of parts for car assembly and the export of finished cars, and in an area with a tradition in engineering. Opened in 1986 the factory will have increased its work force to the 3000 needed to produce the planned 25 000 cars per year by 1991.

Many other jobs have been created in component factories elsewhere in Britain. In late 1989 Nissan announced that their new European car technology research centre would be built 'in the Washington area'.

Toyota at Derby

At present overseas car firms, like Nissan, are allowed to compete in the British market if their product is assembled here. New EC rules, to be introduced in 1992, state that to have unrestricted access to these markets at least 60% of a car must be manufactured within EC countries. Toyota, Japan's largest transnational car company, had therefore to seek a site within the EC if they wished to continue to sell cars in that market. When fully completed, their car plant is expected to produce over 20 000 cars a year, and to employ 6000 people (half of whom would be in component manufacturing). The selected site was at Burnaston, near Derby (Figure 7.27).

Using the information in Figure 7.27 and comparing it with Nissan in Washington what are 1) the physical and 2) the human and economic attractions of the site at Burnaston?

Figure 7.26 An industrial estate near Cramlington New Town

Figure 7.27 The Burnaston greenfield site, Derby

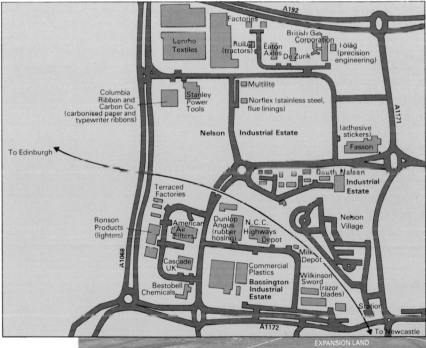

○ CITY GROWTH AND PATTERNS

The first sizeable urban settlements in Britain were developed in Roman times, and since then the British have increasingly moved into towns and cities to live. The real period of urbanisation began with the Industrial Revolution, and, as Figure 8.1 shows, now over 90% of our population live in towns of over 10 000, and about 70% in settlements exceeding 100 000. In the nineteenth century, new arrivals to a city were packed into cramped terraced housing whereas in the twentieth century, in order to give people more space and pleasanter environments, urban areas have grown outwards (urban sprawl) at an alarming rate. Look at Figure 8.2 which shows the size of London at various times since 1800. What was the distance across London in 1800, in 1914 and in 1980? At that rate how big might London be by the time you retire from work?

As many towns and cities throughout Britain have grown in size, neighbouring settlements have become merged to form conurbations, and in doing so have left no farmland or open space between them.

Why people move into cities

- More and better paid jobs.
- Better housing.
- Better services such as schools, hospitals and libraries.
- More entertainment.
- Better transport facilities.
- The work place is nearer, thus reducing time, distance and cost from home.
- Better shopping facilities.

Can you add to this list? What do you think are the problems of living in large cities?

Urban models

It has been suggested that towns do not grow in a haphazard way, but that they show certain generalised characteristics. For example, Burgess (Figure 8.3) suggested that most towns grew outward in a concentric pattern, whereas Hoyt (Figure 8.3) thought a 'wedge' shape was more typical of their growth. A model is a theoretical framework which may not actually exist, but which helps to explain the reality. Can you produce a model for your own local town or city?

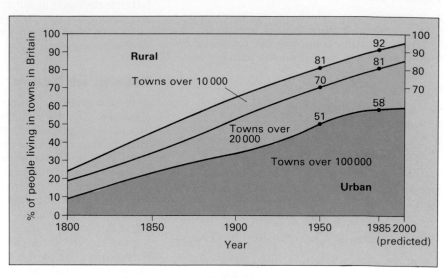

Figure 8.1 The growth of urban population

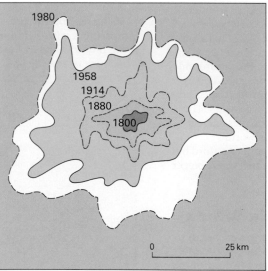

Figure 8.2 The growth of London

Figure 8.3 Two urban models

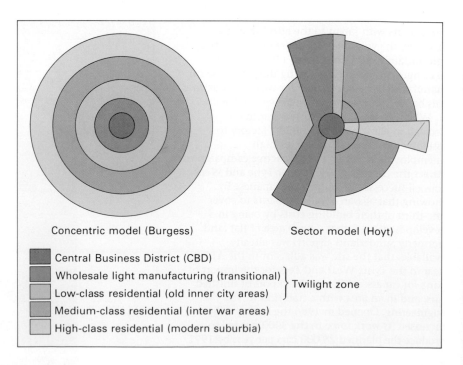

Concentric model (Burgess)   Sector model (Hoyt)

■ Central Business District (CBD)
■ Wholesale light manufacturing (transitional) ⎫
■ Low-class residential (old inner city areas) ⎬ Twilight zone
■ Medium-class residential (inter war areas) ⎭ (should be on appropriate line)
□ High-class residential (modern suburbia)

Location of residential environments: Sheffield

Look at Figure 8.4 which shows eight different housing zones from the CBD to the remote rural areas. How does this compare with the models in Figure 8.3? And how does this compare with your own local town or city?

Figure 8.4 Residential environments in Sheffield

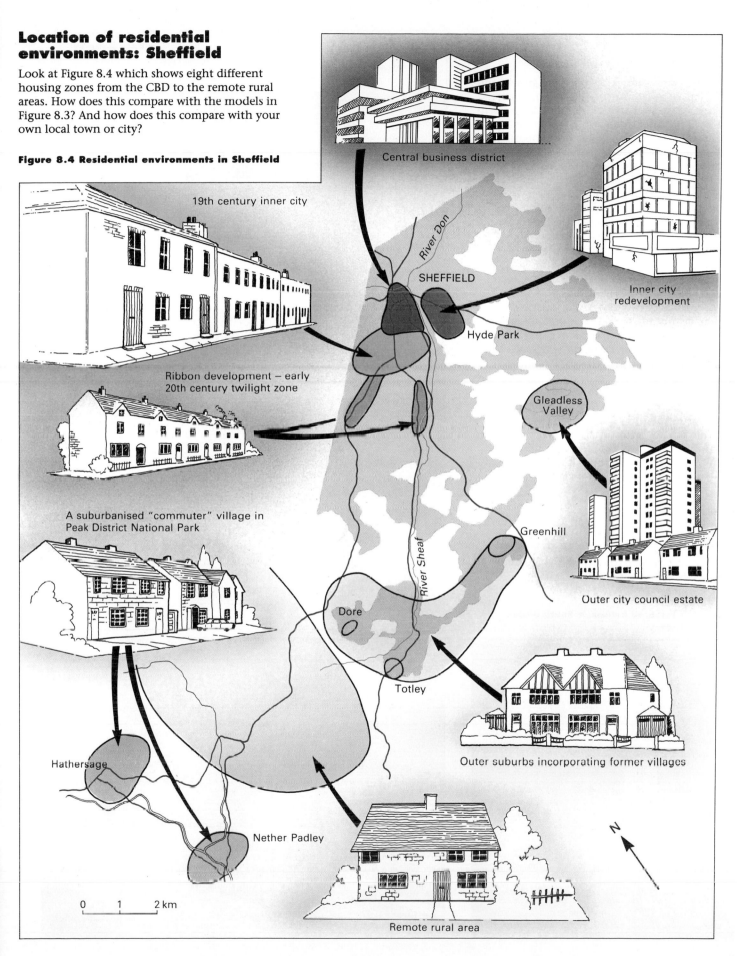

Central business district

19th century inner city

Inner city redevelopment

River Don

SHEFFIELD

Hyde Park

Ribbon development – early 20th century twilight zone

Gleadless Valley

A suburbanised "commuter" village in Peak District National Park

Greenhill

Outer city council estate

River Sheaf

Dore

Hathersage

Totley

Nether Padley

Outer suburbs incorporating former villages

Remote rural area

N

0   1   2 km

◐ OLD INNER CITY AREAS

The nineteenth century saw the rapid growth and expansion of towns which were near to mineral reserves, coastal estuaries and existing large towns. The rapid influx of workers into these towns meant a big demand for quick, cheap housing, and so builders constructed as many houses as possible in a small area which resulted in high density housing with an overcrowded population. The houses were built in long straight rows and in terraces (Figure 8.7). In those days of non-planning, few amenities were provided either in the house (e.g. no indoor WC, bathroom, sewerage, electricity) or around it (e.g. no open space and no gardens).

The worst kind of houses were the so-called 'back-to-back' houses (Figure 8.5) which often only consisted of two rooms: a living room/kitchen downstairs and one bedroom upstairs. These houses were built around a central courtyard in which would be the single WC and single cold water tap for perhaps 20 families (Figure 8.5).Most of the houses of this period were built as closely as possible to the factory where the inhabitants worked, since this was before the days of public transport. The houses soon became blackened by the smoke from the factories, and their inhabitants' health ruined by fumes.

In spite of these conditions and hazards these inner city areas did have advantages:

- The houses were cheap to buy or rent and their rates were low.
- They were near to places of work.
- They developed a strong community spirit.
- They later became convenient for the shops and jobs found in the CBD.

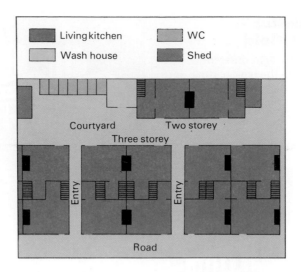

Figure 8.5 Plan of back to back housing

| Living kitchen | WC |
| Wash house | Shed |

Courtyard · Two storey · Three storey · Entry · Entry · Road

Figure 8.6 Back yard of nineteenth century housing in Carlisle

Figure 8.8 Back lane to terraced housing in Carlisle

Figure 8.7 Terraced houses, a South Wales mining village

Land use in the inner city

Figure 8.9 shows the layout and some of the land uses in an inner city area of the early 1980s.

■ Calculate the number of houses in the square shown. This will tell you the housing density of an area. On average in Britain three people live in every house. How many might live within this 100 metre grid square?

■ Notice the grid-iron street layout.

■ Notice the rows of terraced houses with their backyards.

■ What evidence is there of industries in the area shown on the map?

■ These industries grew up as near to the river as possible. Why was this?

■ Notice the railway (now disused).

■ Is there much evidence of open space?

Quality of the environment

Figure 8.10 is a typical street found in many inner city areas.
Notice:

■ The brick-built, nineteenth century terraced Victorian housing now over a hundred years old.

■ The front doors opening straight onto the street.

■ The lack of gardens or other areas of open space.

■ The street parking due to a lack of garages (these houses were built before the invention of the motorcar).

■ The poor quality of the roads and pavements.

■ The nearness to the large factory, and the problems of noise and air pollution from it.

■ The intermixture of houses and industry.

■ Two small areas of wasteland where some houses have been pulled down.

■ A corner shop (not easily visible).

By the early 1980s many of the back-to-back and large rows of terraced houses had been pulled down as slum clearance, or in readiness for redevelopment (Figure 8.11). Many of the original industries had closed down or moved to better sites leaving large areas of derelict land and abandoned works and warehouses. It was in these deprived inner city areas with their poor quality housing, poor schools, lack of jobs, large immigrant groups, limited recreational and social amenities, and the threat of the bulldozer that the riots of the early 1980s occurred. Although each individual area had its own local causes for outbreaks of violence, many root causes had been identified for several decades, and yet far too little money or planning had been devoted to these inner cities.

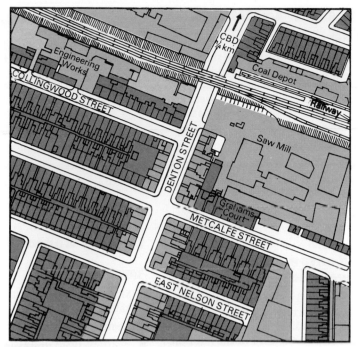

Housing   Transport

Open space and gardens   Wasteland

Industry   Services (schools, shops)

Figure 8.9 Land use in an inner city area — Carlisle (top)

Figure 8.10 Old inner city area — Carlisle (middle)

Figure 8.11 Slum clearance in Maryhill, Glasgow

○ OUTER CITY COUNCIL ESTATES

As local councils cleared the worst of the slums from their inner city areas in the 1950s and 1960s, many residents were rehoused on large council estates on the fringes of the city. Attempts were made to vary the type and size of accommodation. These took the following forms:

- High-rise tower blocks, often of 10-20 storeys.
- Low-rise tower blocks, usually 3-5 storeys high. These were built nearer the city boundaries, where there was more land space.
- Single-storey terraces with some gardens and car parking space.

The North Kenton Council Estate, Newcastle upon Tyne

The North Kenton Council Estate, one of the largest post-war housing schemes undertaken by Newcastle Corporation, is situated in the north-western part of the city on the edge of the built-up area. Most of the estate was built between 1953 and 1959, mainly on agricultural land. It was one of the last 'green field' sites to be completed in Newcastle before the redevelopment of the 'twilight' areas in the city and the construction of estates and new towns outside the city boundary.

Most of the 8000 people living on the estate were rehoused from slums of older dwellings in the congested inner city areas of Newcastle. The types of dwellings in which they were housed is shown in Figure 8.12.

The land use of the estate is shown in Figure 8.13. Notice in particular the proximity of large factories, the large park in the centre, the location of the various types of housing, the range of services (e.g. church, schools, shops) and the curving central road used as a bus route.

North Kenton, like any other area, also had its environmental advantages and disadvantages.

Types and numbers of dwellings on the North Kenton Estate	
One storey self-contained, old persons' dwellings	76
Two storey self-contained houses	970
Three storey maisonettes and flates	438
Four storey flats for single females	24
Five storey maisonettes	120
Also old persons' dwellings on ground floors of the three and five storey maisonettes	282
	1910

Housing density was 44 dwellings per hectare which was about average for a council estate on the edge of an urban area

Figure 8.12 Housing data — North Kenton estate, Newcastle upon Tyne

1 North Kenton in 1980

Advantages

- Modern indoor amenities (WCs, hot water, baths).
- Nearness to a local shopping parade.
- Nearness to an industrial estate.
- Nearness to schools.
- No smoke or industrial pollution.
- Nearness to open country.
- 'Greens' left near to most blocks of houses.
- A large centrally situated park.
- Local amenities such as a clinic, library, church, surgery, public houses.
- A bus route running through the centre of the estate.
- Old peoples' dwellings and self-contained two-storey houses with a degree of privacy.
- Apart from the main bus route through the centre, much of the area is traffic-free.

Disadvantages

- Poor quality housing even though only about 35 years old.
- The pressures from living in high-rise flats.

Figure 8.13 Land use — North Kenton estate

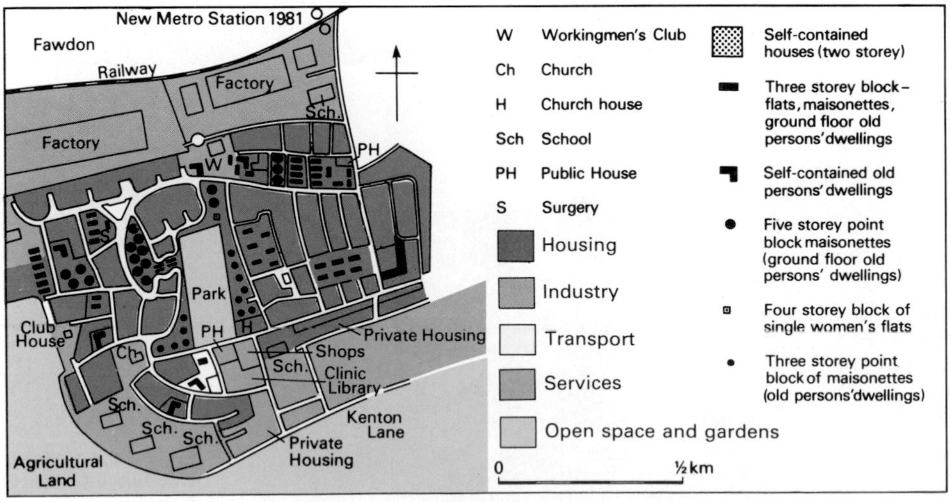

- Flats were not high enough to warrant a lift.
- Lack of gardens and garages.
- Lack of usable open space (Figure 8.13).
- Vandalism of windows and telephones.
- The main shopping centre in the CBD is far away.
- Lack of amenities and organised entertainment for younger children and teenagers.
- Insufficient local jobs, so people had to travel far to find alternative employment.
- Many unskilled, semi-skilled workers made for a high unemployment rate on the estate.
- The elderly found it difficult to adapt to a new environment and to younger neighbours.
- There was generally an unfriendly atmosphere compared with that of the original inner city areas.
- The three-storey buildings had often been vandalised, several had to be demolished, whilst others were boarded up and vacant.
- Several areas of walls were attractively painted, but shops had either wire netting or boards to protect their windows.
- Many houses were damp and few had central heating.
- Concern was expressed by local residents on 'levels of educational disadvantage, social stress and vandalism'.

2 North Kenton in 1990

The North Kenton Project Team was set up in April 1982 by Newcastle City Housing Department as part of its plan to help improve the quality of life on the estate. The Project Team provides an intensive housing management service to the estate, as well as aiming to encourage community development and to help co-ordinate public services on the estate.

Figure 8.14 North Kenton - three storey buildings

- The five-storey buildings had been improved, were in a good state of repair and had been turned into single person accommodation (Figure 8.15). Controlled entry systems had improved security against burglary and mugging.
- The remaining three-storey buildings had been modernised. The demolished property was often replaced by sheltered housing and landscaped areas.
- The Council agreed in 1984 to install central heating and wall insulation in all houses to reduce damp.
- An adventure playground had been built (1984) and also a community/sports hall (1985).
- Many more trees had been planted and car parking spaces provided. Residents were loaned equipment free of charge to maintain their gardens.
- North Kenton Health Project runs keep fit classes and first aid courses. There is a Youth Advisory Service.

Other outer city council estates

Figure 8.17 shows an outer city council estate which was built in the early 1960s. For this estate fewer high-rise flats were built, and many lower buildings were built with the contour of the land, while many trees were left standing.

Figure 8.15 North Kenton - five storey buildings (top left)

Figure 8.16 Modern houses in Kenton (middle)

Figure 8.17 An outer city council estate(bottom)

INNER CITY REDEVELOPMENTS

When in the 1950s and 1960s vast areas of inner cities were cleared by bulldozers many of the displaced inhabitants either moved to council estates near the city boundary, or were rehoused in huge high-rise tower blocks which were created on the sites of the old terraced houses (Figure 8.18).

The Cebus Bory Tower block estate was opened in 1968 in the London Borough of Hackney. From the start they were damp and by 1971 many of the seven blocks were uninhabitable. They were dynamited in 1983 and replaced by 'old fashioned' houses with gardens. Other tower blocks, especially on Merseyside, have suffered similar fates.

Figure 8.18 High rise flats — Glasgow

The reasons for building high-rise flats were:

- The local authorities found these high-rise flats cheap to build and quick to erect (as were the nineteenth century houses they had replaced).
- To save space by building upwards.
- To create areas of open space between the tower blocks.
- To provide modern indoor amenities such as WCs, hot running water and central heating.
- To provide freedom from industrial traffic and yet to allow easy access to jobs and shops in the nearby CBD.
- To keep together the community spirit of the nineteenth century communities.
- To create panoramic views. (How many storeys do the flats in Figure 8.18 have?)

These high-rise flats were built in good faith for **economic advantage**.

High-rise flats proved to be a failure because:

- Inhuman conditions gave a total lack of neighbourliness.
- These ugly buildings were also surrounded by non-usable areas of open space.
- The elderly felt trapped, especially those living above the ground floor.
- There was a lack of play areas and amenities for youngsters.
- Mugging in passageways prevented many elderly inhabitants venturing out; and there was a high level of vandalism and noise.
- The mental strain and depression amongst the inhabitants rapidly increased.
- The poor quality of the buildings. Indeed, one tower block in London (Ronan Point) collapsed, and several others (e.g. Oak and Eldon flats in Liverpool) have been demolished.
- There still existed an extremely high population density (e.g. Hyde Park, Sheffield had 400 persons per hectare).

It was only later therefore that the inhabitants found living in the flats to be a **social disadvantage**.

The Byker Scheme (Newcastle upon Tyne)

More recent inner city developments have seen a greater awareness for the person who will eventually be rehoused there. The Byker scheme exemplified this new awareness. Here the architects moved into an undertaker's shop in 'Old Byker' and planned, together with the local residents, the demolition of the area and the rebuilding of the 'New Byker'. The scheme was to build the 'Byker Wall' of brightly coloured bricks (Figure 8.19) in order to protect the area from the noise of a proposed urban motorway (which was never built, but which has now become part of the Metro rail system) whilst inside were to be areas of low-rise development grouped into small communities.

The Byker Wall: The north face (Figure 8.19)

- This section of the 'wall' faces the Metro and acts as a noise barrier.
- Five different colours highlight vehicle and pedestrian access points as well as disguising the brickwork.
- Only kitchen and bathroom windows (double-glazed) face north, and so the other windows avoid the coldest winds.
- The 'wall' varies in height (3-8 storeys) and has curves (thereby reducing the scale of both length and height).
- It is next to the Byker Metro Station.

The Byker Wall: The south face (Figure 8.20)

- All living rooms, bedrooms and dining rooms are on this south side, which is the sunnier, lighter and quieter side.
- For similar reasons, all access decks and individual balconies are on this side.
- It has a bright and more varied colour scheme which breaks up the overall scale of the block.
- The longest, uninterrupted straight section is only seven dwellings in length.
- Each ground floor flat has its own small garden.
- Most dwellings are maisonettes, but there are a few one- or two-person dwellings. Families with children are placed on ground floors; single persons and childless couples have higher dwellings.
- Access decks are made from brightly coloured timber and the low roofs are made from translucent corrugated material, which makes the decks light, airy and reasonably sheltered.
- Old buildings are incorporated into the wall, such as the Shipley Baths and the community centre.

Byker low-rise development (Figure 8.21)

- Pedestrianised development — no traffic in most areas.
- Most houses have small gardens, so the trees and greenery help to improve the environment.
- Different colours are allotted to houses to create sub-neighbourhoods.
- Only limited parking spaces and garages exist as few Byker residents own cars.
- Local 'greens' for public use. These include small sitting/picnic and play areas. A scheme begun in 1976 paid local residents £150 per year to maintain these greens. Consequently vandalism has been reduced.
- Old St. Lawrence's Church, old pubs and clubs, the baths, and a community centre are incorporated into the new area.
- A new local shopping centre has been built.

Figure 8.19 Byker Wall — the north face

Figure 8.20 Byker Wall — the south face

Figure 8.21 Neighbourhood units within the estate at Byker

⊙ SUBURBIA

Inner suburbia

The nineteenth century factory owners and managers lived further away from the city centre and industrial zones. They built 'squares' nearer the edge of cities, or very large houses with many rooms, and even attics and a basement (for the servants) alongside main road. The road access was important as these residents could afford either their own coach and horses or to travel on horse-drawn buses. These properties, which make up the 'twilight zone', have either undergone extensive modernisation or have been turned into 'service' buildings for doctors, dentists and small insurance companies. They have also been turned into flats (especially in university towns) or have been pulled down for road widening (Figure 8.22).

Outer suburbia

The rapid outward growth of cities began with the introduction of public transport, a growth which accelerated with the popularity of the private car. This outward growth (also known as urban sprawl) led to the construction of numerous private, 'car-based' suburbs.

The houses built in the outer suburbs before the Second World War are characterised by their front and back gardens, garages and usually are semi-detached with bay windows (Figure 8.23).

The modern estates, which in the present day are situated on the city fringe, have, however, quite differing types and styles of housing (Figure 8.24).

Why live in suburbia?

The major reasons for living in suburbia include:

- Larger, better quality housing.
- Modern indoor amenities (e.g. running water, a WC and bath, central heating and modern kitchens).
- Garages.
- Gardens in the front and back.
- Mainly traffic-free roads (having neither through traffic nor heavy traffic) which means less accidents.
- Tree-lined roads.
- Areas of public open space are nearer, as is the open countryside.
- Freedom from industrial noise and fumes.
- Lower density housing (Figure 8.26). Can you estimate how many people live in the 100 metre square shown in Figure 8.26?

The disadvantages of suburbia include:

- Distance from work.
- The cost of extra petrol and bus fares; and the extra time required for getting to and from work.

- Distance from shops, especially the large city centre areas.
- Lack of indoor entertainment, such as cinemas and theatres; and fewer libraries, doctors and dentists.
- High cost of houses.

Figure 8.22 Inner suburbs — Carlisle

Figure 8.24 Modern outer city housing estate, Folkestone, Kent

Figure 8.23 Outer suburbia, South-west London (above)

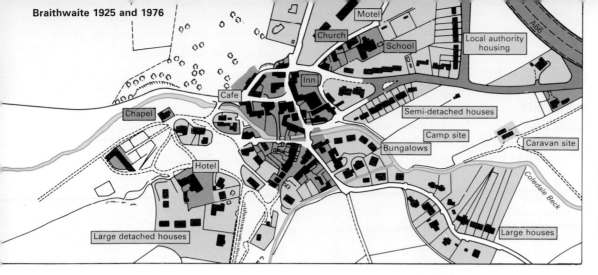

Braithwaite 1925 and 1976

Motel
Church
School
Local authority housing
Inn
Cafe
Semi-detached houses
Chapel
Camp site
Bungalows
Caravan site
Hotel
Coledale Beck
Large detached houses
Large houses

**Figure 8.25
A 'suburbanised' village
in the Lake District**

━━━ New or improved roads

▦ Buildings and built up areas in 1925

▨ Buildings and built up areas dating 1925–1976

0   100 metres

Movement out of the city

Can you explain the following diagram?

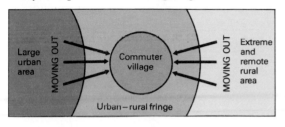

Large urban area — MOVING OUT — Commuter village — MOVING OUT — Extreme and remote rural area

Urban–rural fringe

Suburbanised villages

In parts of the developed world there has been a reversal of the movement to large urban areas, and groups of people have moved out into surrounding villages. This has led to a change in the character of such settlements and to their being called suburbanised (because they adopt some of the characteristics of the nearby urban areas) or commuter-dormitory towns (because many residents who live and sleep there travel to the nearby towns and cities for work).

These often consist of a core of old, stone cottages (now mostly expensively modernised) surrounded by estates of modern 'semis' and detached houses. (Figure 8.25.)

Unplanned and unchecked growth has often led to a total change in the character of the village. For example, the commuters, who live in the village but work in nearby towns and cities now outnumber the original inhabitants. In addition to this, villages which have grown rapidly find a big strain is put upon such services as the village school and shop. The increase in the number of cars means congestion on narrow lanes or the building of new roads. As private transport grows, there is a fall in demand for public transport. Farmland around the village is either built upon or leads to conflict between the farmers and those people wishing to use it for recreation. The newcomers, often wealthy, formerly urban residents who can afford the new, larger houses (or can convert old buildings) and the cost of transport to work, shops and amenities often take over the 'social' life of the village.

Eventually the village may turn into a dormitory of the big city, totally losing its individuality. With the influx of more people demanding a place to live, house prices soar. As

Lansdowne Crescent
Beech Grove
Nursery
Knowefield
Knowefield
KNOWEFIELD

**Figure 8.26 An inter-war
(1930s) suburban estate**

prices become too high for the local inhabitants, houses are bought up as second homes by city dwellers wishing to escape from their own environment. This problem of second homes exists in Scotland and the Lake District National Park, but nowhere is it more acute than in Wales.

Remoter rural areas — second homes

The Welsh village of Rhyd (Gwynedd) is typical of many of these remoter areas. Only five of the twenty houses in the village are permanently occupied. The others are all holiday homes, only used by their owners at weekends or during the summer, when families from the affluent parts of England take up residence.

Rhyd has everything as a place in which to spend the summer. Breathtakingly beautiful, it rests on a shoulder of the Moelwyn Mountains five miles from the magnificent beaches of Cardigan Bay and a short drive from the best scenery in Snowdonia.

But for the handful of people still clinging to a year-round existence there is little material cheer. As employment prospects in the area declined after the war families were forced to move away in search of work.

Their homes were quickly bought by the well-heeled from across Offa's Dyke at prices beyond the reach of the remaining farm workers and quarrymen.

○ NEW TOWNS

First generation 1946-60

Following on from the Abercrombie Report of 1944, the New Towns Act, 1946 was an attempt to regulate population movement by creating newly planned settlements to relieve overcrowding in such large cities as London and Glasgow (Figure 8.27). These new towns (Figure 8.28) were designed to take in up to 80 000 persons and to be 'self-contained and balanced communities for work and living'. They were financed by the Government and, with the exception of Corby which was built to provide houses for the then rapidly growing steel works, they provided:

- New houses to relieve overcrowding in large cities, and homes for those people displaced by slum clearances.
- New and varied jobs for their communities.
- New services such as schools, hospitals, and shopping centres.
- Self-contained neighbourhoods.
- Areas of planned open space in an attempt to provide a 'Garden City' environment.

Second generation 1960-70

These new towns were more widely distributed over Britain (Figure 8.27) and like the first generation new towns they also did not exceed 80 000 inhabitants. These towns were built for a variety of reasons:

- As overspill towns for nearby conurbations (e.g. Skelmersdale and Redditch).
- In areas of growth industries (e.g. Glenrothes on the Fifeshire coalfield).
- To attract jobs to areas of high unemployment (e.g. Washington and Craigavon).
- To improve environments ruined by previous industrial development (e.g. Killingworth).
- A major difference in their layout was the greater number of roads and car parks, together with pedestrianised shopping parades.

Third generation 1970-

These were 'New Cities' which could reach a population of 250 000. The new cities, Milton Keynes, Telford and Central Lancashire are each the amalgamation of several small centres. It is hoped that these three will become 'Growth Points' for their region.

- They have widespread industrial estates.
- They are based on efficient communications.
- They have widespread leisure amenities from indoor sports centres to country parks.

Figure 8.28 New Towns — population

Expanded towns

These are existing towns which have been selected for expansion and funded by both national and local government. These are favoured as being less costly to create than totally new towns.

Figure 8.27 The location of New Towns

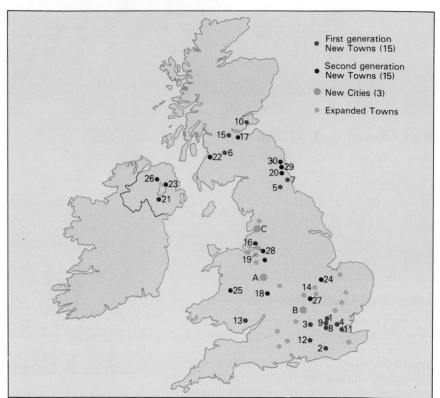

Map No	Town	Year of designation	Population		
			At designation (000's)	1981 Census (000's)	Ultimate (unlikely to be reached) (000's)
1	Stevenage	1946	7.0	74.4	105
2	Crawley	1947	10.0	47.5	79
3	Hemel Hempstead	1947	21.0	76.3	80
4	Harlow	1947	4.5	79.2	90
5	Aycliffe	1947	0.06	24.7	45
6	East Kilbride	1947	2.5	71.3	100
7	Peterlee	1948	0.2	22.8	30
8	Hatfield	1948	8.5	25.1*	30
9	Welwyn Garden City	1948	18.5	40.5	50
10	Glenrothes	1948	1.1	48.2	70
11	Basildon	1949	25.0	94.3	140
12	Bracknell	1949	5.0	48.8	55
13	Cwmbran	1949	12.0	44.3	55
14	Corby	1950	15.7	47.8	83
15	Cumbernauld	1955	3.5	32.5	100
16	Skelmersdale	1961	10.0	39.1	80
17	Livingston	1962	2.1	36.5	100
18	Redditch	1964	32.0	63.7	90
19	Runcorn	1964	28.5	63.8	100
20	Washington	1964	20.0	47.4	80
21	Craigavon	1965	40.0	71.0	180
22	Irvine	1966	40.0	55.2	120
23	Antrim	1966	7.0	45.3	50
24	Peterborough	1967	80.5	114.1	185
25	Newtown	1967	5.5	8.7	13
26	Ballymena	1967	21.0	54.7	80
27	Northampton	1968	131.0	156.9	230
28	Warrington	1968	124.0	134.3	230
29	Killingworth	1963	7.0	10.2	17
30	Cramlington	1963	14.0	27.1 1985 est.	62
A	Telford	1963	70.0	103.4 104	250
B	Milton Keynes	1967	40.0	96.1 107	250
C	Central Lancashire	1970	235.0	247.2 249	430

*Decreased 1971-1981

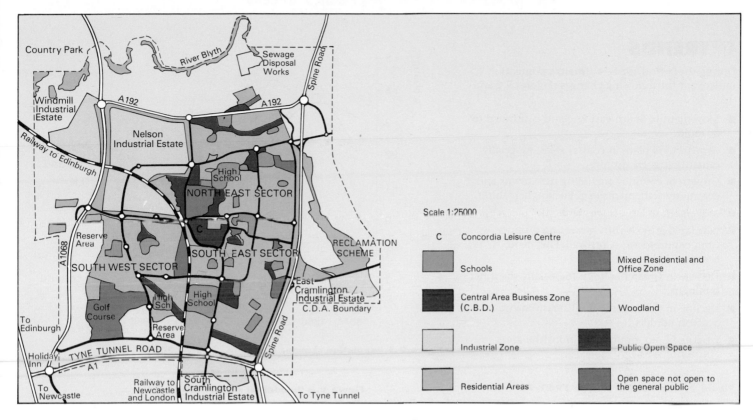

Scale 1:25000

C   Concordia Leisure Centre

Schools

Central Area Business Zone (C.B.D.)

Industrial Zone

Residential Areas

Mixed Residential and Office Zone

Woodland

Public Open Space

Open space not open to the general public

Cramlington New Town

Land use in a new town is carefully planned, and the major aspects of Cramlington New Town are shown in Figure 8.29.

■ An outer quadrangle of dual carriageway roads with roundabout access points. There is also a main North–South and East–West route through the CBD.

■ It has an inner ring of main roads.

■ The industrial estates are located:

   1 On the edge of Cramlington New Town away from residential areas to limit noise, pollution and traffic.

   2 Near enough to residential areas to limit length and time of journey to work.

   3 Next to main roads and the railway for transport.

■ The screening of main roads by wooded areas.

■ The CBD with its traffic-free, undercover shopping parade also has a large leisure centre, library, police HQ and large car parking areas (Figure 12.11).

■ Office areas are adjacent to the CBD for accessibility.

■ Three sectors (the fourth is industrial) are based on the 'Neighbourhood Unit' concept, each having its own high school, junior schools, and open space (play areas and recreation grounds).

■ It is near to the open country and there is also a nearby country park and the Northumberland National Park.

A neighbourhood unit in a New Town

The model of a neighbourhood unit (Figure 8.30) shows that by having its own open space, community centre and shops, it can:

■ Reduce the need for transport to these amenities.

■ Minimise cost and time in getting to these amenities.

■ Ensure easier and safer access for the young and elderly.

■ Help to develop a local community spirit.

■ Reduce the overuse and congestion of one major amenity in that town.

Figure 8.29 Land use in Cramlington New Town

Figure 8.30 A neighbourhood unit in a New Town

Note: New Towns using this idea are made up of many such neighbourhood units

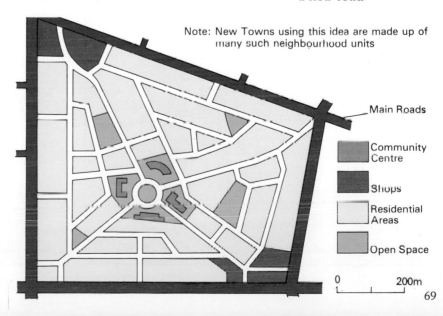

Main Roads

Community Centre

Shops

Residential Areas

Open Space

0   200m

○ TRENDS

During the period 1951-71 Britain's population underwent the following changes (Figures 9.1 and 9.2):

■ Movement to South-east England continued to be rapid.

■ Growth took place in coastal areas, especially estuaries (e.g. Hampshire).

■ Growth of counties, including new towns and commuter settlements (e.g. Buckinghamshire).

■ Movement to large towns and cities.

■ Less rapid growth with increasing distance from conurbations (Cornwall, Gwynedd, Scottish Highlands).

■ Decline in Greater London (especially the inner boroughs).

■ Decline in the extreme rural areas (Powys, Scottish Borders).

■ Decline in old mining and industrial areas (Tyne and Wear).

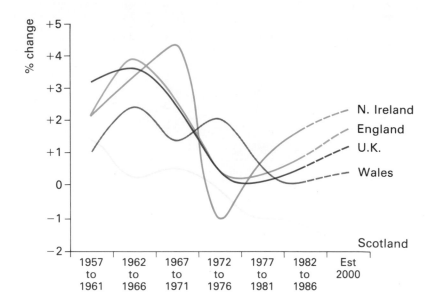

Figure 9.1 Population changes in the UK, 1956-2000

Figure 9.2 Population change 1961-71

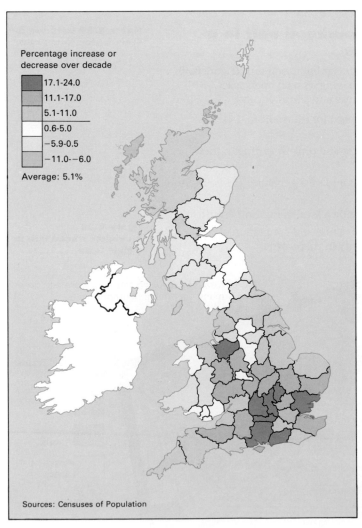

Sources: Censuses of Population

Figure 9.3 Population change, 1971-81

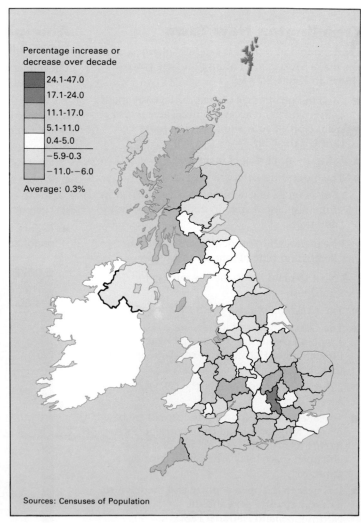

Sources: Censuses of Population

Between 1971 and 1981 (Figure 9.3) the following changes occurred:

- Largest increases occurred in rural areas with small towns (Norfolk, Cornwall).
- Increase in North-east Scotland linked with North Sea oil.
- Increase in many counties some distance from conurbations, and especially if these counties included new towns (Buckinghamshire, Shropshire).
- Gains in areas with no conurbations (South-west England, East Anglia).
- Biggest decrease in Greater London (including the outer boroughs).
- Decline in all conurbations and the largest cities (Bristol, Nottingham, Cardiff).
- Decline continued in old mining and industrial areas (Durham, West Glamorgan).
- Decline began to take place in South-east England (Surrey).

Between 1981 and 1986 (Figure 9.4) the general trends were similar to those of 1971-1981 except that:

- there was less overall mobility with no area gaining over 7.2% (Buckinghamshire) and none losing more than 3.6% (Scottish Islands).
- the decrease in the movement to the South-east of England was probably due mainly to the considerable increase in southern house prices,
- the more favoured areas were still the 'Shire' counties surrounding London, and the south coast,
- the least favoured areas were still the conurbations of old industrial areas.

Britain's ageing population

Every census this century has shown that people in the UK are living longer and that fewer children are being born — the latter with the exception of the post-war baby boom reflected by the slight increase in children under the age of five in 1951.

During the 1970s, nearly a million more people became pensioners, and by 1981, almost a quarter of all households consisted solely of elderly people. By 1990, one in five people qualified for a pension, and there was a growing demand for extra and improved services for this age group (e.g. medical care and specialist accommodation) (Figure 9.5).

The falling birth rate reflected the recession of the late 1970s and early 1980s, the decrease in family life, an increase in the number of women wishing to pursue a career, and a growing desire for material possessions.

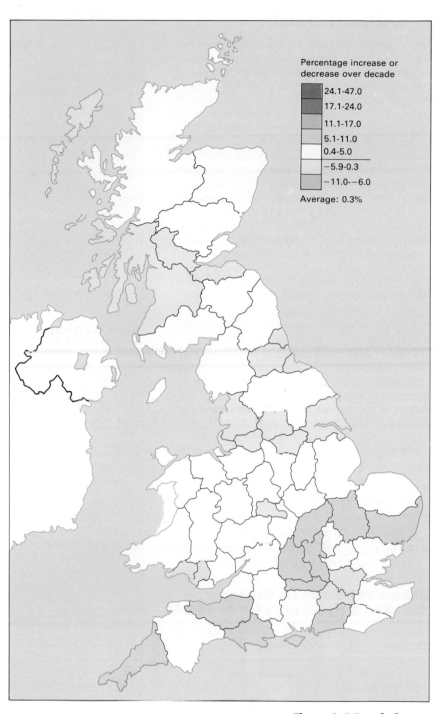

Figure 9.4 Population change, 1981-86

Percentage increase or decrease over decade

- 24.1-47.0
- 17.1-24.0
- 11.1-17.0
- 5.1-11.0
- 0.4-5.0
- -5.9-0.3
- -11.0--6.0

Average: 0.3%

Figure 9.5 The UK's ageing population

Year	% Under 5	% Under 18	% over pensionable age	% over 75
1911	10.7	37.2	5.3	1.5
1931	7.7	35.3	7.4	2.1
1951	8.6	35.0	10.9	3.5
1971	8.1	36.4	13.2	4.7
1986	6.4	31.9	18.1	6.5

● URBAN DECAY

One of the consequences of the 1971 Census was the highlighting of urban decay in inner city areas. The problem was most noticeable in the conurbations, with Clydeside being top of the national urban deprivation league (Figure 9.6) in terms of the lack of basic amenities, overcrowding and unemployment. Following the census, it was decided to abandon plans to develop Scotland's sixth new town at Stonehouse as this would have provided yet another rival source for housing and jobs to Glasgow. Instead it was decided to concentrate resources on redeveloping the inner area of Glasgow. This project, started in May 1976, was called GEAR (Glasgow Eastern Area Renewal) and became the most ambitious urban renewal programme in Britain. It was run jointly by Glasgow District Council, Strathclyde Regional Council, and the Scottish Special Housing Agency (SSHA). The public's view of the problems and priorities for the area varied. In Camlachie the main concern was the atmospheric pollution from a local chemical works, while in Dalmarnock, attention focused on the lack of local shopping. Generally, however, the major issues were seen as crime and vandalism, the physical environment, shopping needs, employment, leisure and recreation, and public transport. The statistics in Figure 9.7 try to show the scale of the problem facing the GEAR Project, and especially those problems facing residents who had remained. By looking at Figure 9.7 can you say:

■ By how much the population declined between 1971 and 1981? Why was this?

■ Which groups of people have remained in GEAR? Why have they remained?

■ What do you consider to be the major problems facing those residents who have remained?

Urban renewal in Glasgow — the GEAR Project, 1976-1983

The GEAR Project was set up to be 'a concentrated plan and programme for the comprehensive regeneration of the East-end of Glasgow in association with the people of the area.'

It had six basic aims:

■ Helping residents to secure employment by giving incentives to firms.

■ Retraining the unemployed, and school leavers with relevant skills and creating jobs and encouraging local firms to develop.

■ Improving the quality of life by introducing projects to improve education, leisure amenities, health and social services.

■ Improving the environment by landscaping, reducing pollution and upgrading housing and roads.

■ Creating better housing by building 3000 new homes and modernising 10 000 properties.

■ Involving, and consulting with, the community.

Figure 9.8 shows the GEAR area in 1983.

Conurbation	Clydeside	West Midlands	Greater Manchester	Merseyside	West Yorkshire	Inner London	Tyne and Wear
Sharing or lacking hot water	15.5	7.5	4.8	5.2	1.7	27.7	2.7
Sharing or lacking a bath	15.6	3.9	6.0	5.0	1.9	28.2	3.1
Lacking inside W.C.	5.9	6.2	13.6	6.8	3.6	7.0	6.0
Without exclusive use of all basic amenities	13.5	4.7	9.6	5.4	2.6	21.7	4.2
Houses with over 1.5 persons per room	37.3	5.6	1.9	1.5	3.0	21.8	1.3
Households with car	25.7	2.9	8.9	5.0	8.6	12.9	7.2
Males unemployed	23.1	2.8	6.1	9.0	4.2	2.9	6.7
Females unemployed	13.7	3.8	5.4	6.2	3.5	6.3	2.9
Population aged 0-14	12.8	5.5	4.3	3.4	3.3	3.5	1.9
Pensioner households	4.8	1.4	3.8	0.9	5.3	4.3	1.4

(Figures expressed as a percentage)

Figure 9.6 Major areas of urban deprivation, 1971

Figure 9.7 Glasgow Eastern Area Renewal (GEAR) — data

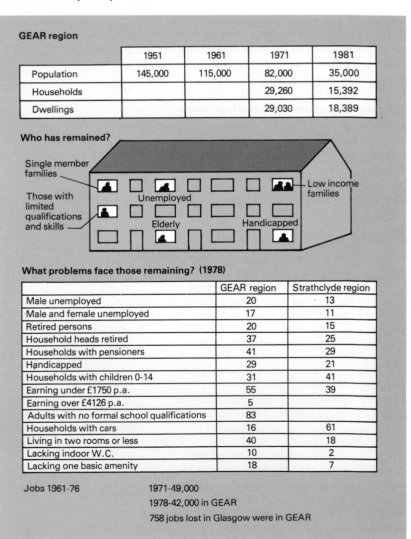

GEAR region

	1951	1961	1971	1981
Population	145,000	115,000	82,000	35,000
Households			29,260	15,392
Dwellings			29,030	18,389

Who has remained?

Single member families
Those with limited qualifications and skills
Unemployed
Elderly
Handicapped
Low income families

What problems face those remaining? (1978)

	GEAR region	Strathclyde region
Male unemployed	20	13
Male and female unemployed	17	11
Retired persons	20	15
Household heads retired	37	25
Households with pensioners	41	29
Handicapped	29	21
Households with children 0-14	31	41
Earning under £1750 p.a.	55	39
Earning over £4126 p.a.	5	
Adults with no formal school qualifications	83	
Households with cars	16	61
Living in two rooms or less	40	18
Lacking indoor W.C.	10	2
Lacking one basic amenity	18	7

Jobs 1961-76
1971-49,000
1978-42,000 in GEAR
758 jobs lost in Glasgow were in GEAR

URBAN RENEWAL

In an attempt to improve living conditions in old inner city areas, local community housing associations have been set up. These are non-profit making societies run by voluntary committees, often under guidance from the local city or district council, to provide accommodation for people in need of housing and to improve existing housing. By registering with the Housing Corporation, a community housing association can obtain government loans and/or grants. The Housing Corporation is a government agency with statutory duties to promote, assist, supervise and finance local community housing associations.
In drawing up any new plan for an area, all groups living there should be considered, e.g. young children, teenagers, couples, the elderly, the disabled, pedestrians, car-drivers, etc.
Study Figure 9.9 which shows the improvements made to one old inner city area. **X** marks the point from which the photo in Figure 8.10 was taken.

1 Which of the groups in the community do you think have been catered for, and which have not?
2 How successful do you think the planners have been in trying to overcome the social, environmental and economic problems of the area?
3 If you were on the local housing association, what further ideas would you put forward to improve the area — bearing in mind that inner city areas are usually short of money?

Figure 9.8 GEAR — Glasgow Eastern Area Renewal

Figure 9.9 An inner-city urban renewal scheme

○ MOVEMENT

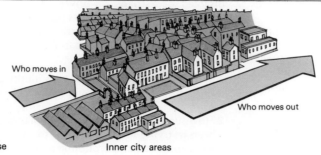

Elderly living on low incomes, no longer with a family, and wishing cheaper housing near to the CBD and other services (shops, library, hospital)

Newly wedded couples with little capital and no family — first time buyers

Poor families with limited resources

Immigrants from overseas especially those with limited money, education and skills

Who moves in

Who moves out

Inner city areas

Those with higher incomes now capable of buying their own homes in suburbia

Those with higher skills and qualifications — especially moving to new towns

Parents with a young family wishing for gardens, open space and larger houses

Figure 9.10 Movement in inner city areas

Who are the immigrants?

Figure 9.11 shows the birthplaces of people resident in the UK in 1971. But this data hides many facts. For example:

■ The majority of UK residents are themselves descended from immigrants: from the Romans, Vikings, Angles and Saxons.

■ The Irish have been settling in Britain (as have the British in Ireland) for many centuries.

■ Many Europeans migrated to the UK during and after the Second World War (1939-45).

■ Old Commonwealth immigrants are from countries (Australia, Canada and New Zealand) originally settled by British emigrants, and whose descendants have returned to Britain.

■ The New Commonwealth includes such countries as India, Sri Lanka, West Indian states and Bangladesh. Most of the inhabitants of these countries, who were coloured and held British passports, were originally encouraged to come to Britain to make up the labour shortage at that time.

The source area of the New Commonwealth immigrants in 1971 according to birthplace, is shown in Figure 9.11. When referring to this data it is also helpful to remember that:

■ Many black and Asian people are not immigrants, but were born in the UK.

■ Since the Second World War, Britain has at various times:

1 Encouraged such immigrants as West Indians to come here to take up poorly paid, unskilled jobs.

2 Accepted British passport holders who were evicted from their home country (e.g. Ugandan Asians).

3 Offered accommodation to such refugees as the Vietnamese boat people.

■ Some immigrants are highly qualified (e.g. doctors).

■ Other immigrants, despite their initial disadvantages, manage to improve in terms of jobs, education and housing.

Figure 9.11 Immigration data

Population of the UK by birthplace (1971 census)

	Population (000's)	%
All countries of birth	53 873	100.00
United Kingdom	50 670	94.05
Irish Republic	709	1.32
Europe	633	1.17
Old Commonwealth (white)	143	0.27
New Commonwealth (black)	1151	2.14
America	131	0.24
Others	436	0.81

Source areas of new commonwealth immigrants (1971—1986)

	1971 %		1986 %
Indians	30.7	Bangladesh, India An Sri Lanka	43.3
Pakistanis	17.2	Pakistan	10.8
West Indians	46.6	Caribbean, Guyana and Belize	13.5
'British' West Africans	5.5	Africa	32.4

New commonwealth immigrants in conurbations (1971)

Conurbation	% black and Asian immigrants in UK	% of total population of that conurbation
Tyneside	0.4	1.7
West Yorkshire	6.4	3.6
Greater Manchester	4.7	4.9
Merseyside	0.5	2.6
East Midlands*	12.0	4.9
West Midlands	14.3	4.9
Greater London	40.5	15.2
Total	78.8	37.8

* East Midlands (Nottingham, Derby, Leicester) is not usually listed as a conurbation
1981 census figures less meaningful as an increasing number of black and Asian members of the community were born in Britain and were not immigrants
1991 census figures will include nationalities of immigrants

The distribution of New Commonwealth immigrants in Sheffield

Figure 9.12 shows the distribution of New Commonwealth immigrants in Sheffield according to the figures from the 1971 Census. As can be seen from the map, immigrants have settled in specific areas. The reasons why immigrants have been attracted to certain areas are given below.

A and B The old inner city

In this area are the nineteenth century terraced houses which are the cheapest to buy and rent. Newly arrived immigrants settle here in place of earlier residents who have moved out to the suburbs and new towns. Many immigrants prefer to live here with others of their own colour, religion, language and custom.

A and A¹ The industrialised Don Valley

This has the added attraction of being near to jobs. Many of these jobs only need limited skills. Traditionally such areas as this offer the least attractive, lowest paid jobs.

C The inner suburbs

These have a much lower concentration of immigrants, but in Sheffield this zone has a higher than average number due to the proximity of the university and hospitals.

D Inner city redevelopment

This area, mainly one of high-rise flats, has a noticeable absence of New Commonwealth immigrants partly due to the long waiting list for council houses, and partly to the reluctance amongst Asians to rent property.

E and E¹ Outer city suburbs and council estates

The only immigrants living in these areas are those who belong to such professional groups as doctors.

The problems facing immigrants in Britain

Although only two out of every ten persons resident in Britain have come directly, or are descended from immigrants from the New Commonwealth, most of them not only live in conurbations, but group together with other members of their own ethnic group in inner city areas.

The segregation of different ethnic groups in British cities results from differences in wealth, class, colour, religion, education and the quality of the environment. While many activities may be positive — such as the Notting Hill Carnival and Brixton's multicultural society, the more usual description, perhaps because it is more 'media worthy' is often negative.

The major problems confronting immigrants will generally result from: language difficulties, cultural differences and racial prejudices. Many members of ethnic minorities have to live in overcrowded poor quality housing, and this leads to racial tension. Unemployment often exceeds 70%, much of it long term. Lower education opportunities and, often, lower expectations, means the inhabitants develop few skills. A lack of money on the part of the inhabitants and the various levels of government means inadequate services. While 'authority' points to the high rate of crime-violence, drugs and muggings — residents point to police harassment. The resultant lack of trust leads to further tension. These problems were highlighted during the 1981 riots in such inner city areas as Toxteth (Merseyside), Moss Side (Greater Manchester) and Brixton (South London) and four years later in Toxteth, Handsworth (Birmingham), Brixton and the Broadwater Farm Estate in Tottenham (London).

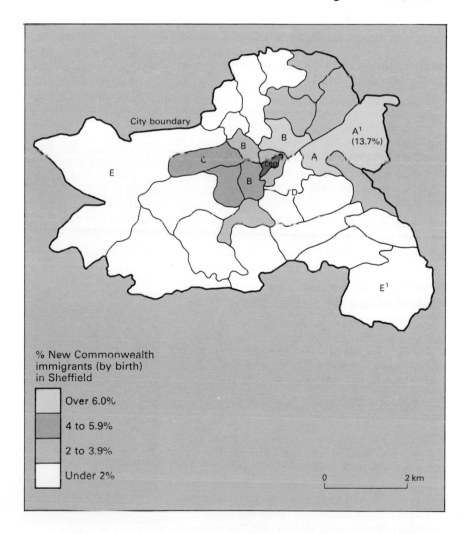

Figure 9.12 Distribution of New Commonwealth immigrants in Sheffield

⬤ PATTERNS

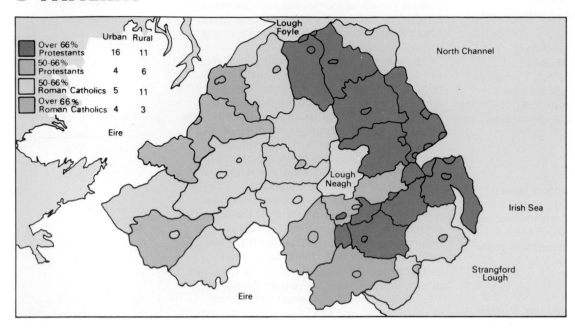

Legend:
	Urban	Rural
Over 66% Protestants	16	11
50-66% Protestants	4	6
50-66% Roman Catholics	5	11
Over 66% Roman Catholics	4	3

Figure 9.13 Population distribution in Northern Ireland

Population distribution in Northern Ireland

Figure 9.13 shows how Northern Ireland can be divided into areas where either Protestants or Roman Catholics are in the majority. Some points about this distribution are:

- The Protestants, who look towards the British mainland economically and politically, tend to dominate in the North and East, and the Roman Catholics, with their links with Eire, dominate in the South and West.

- Protestants tend to be more numerous in urban areas, and Roman Catholics in the rural districts.

Can you account for the pattern shown in Figure 9.13, and can you suggest what some of the resultant problems might be?

Some reasons for the distribution of population

This map (Figure 9.13), however, fails to include many other underlying reasons for the divisions and distributions of people in Northern Ireland. Some of these reasons are:

The age-sex differences between urban and rural areas

In Figure 9.14 figures are given, in the form of age-sex 'pyramids', for the rural and urban population of Northern Ireland. From this information it is clear that in rural areas:

- There are more elderly and retired people (A on graph) than in urban areas. In Britain many villages have as many as 25% retired persons and 20% living alone.

- There are fewer young people moving to urban areas hoping for work (B on graph) compared to a decade earlier.

Urban areas show:

- More younger people are moving into these areas for work (C on graph), and they, in turn, have produced

- Many younger children (D on graph).

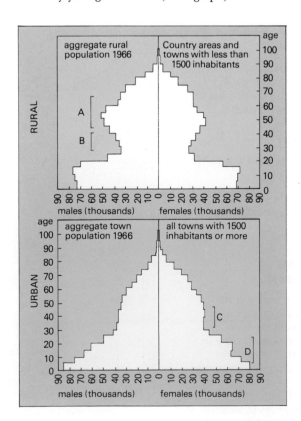

Figure 9.14 Age-sex pyramids, Northern Ireland

Socio-economic differences between the Protestants and Roman Catholics

The majority of professional and skilled people in Northern Ireland tend to be Protestants. Traditionally it is they who have, for example, filled most jobs at the Harland & Wolff shipyard in Belfast.

On the other hand, the majority of semi-skilled and unskilled workers tend to be Roman Catholics. This group also finds work more difficult to obtain, and suffers first from recessions and job losses.

The uneven distribution of Protestants and Roman Catholics in Belfast

Figure 9.15 shows the uneven distribution between Protestants and Roman Catholics in Belfast. Notice how the Roman Catholics, although only about 26% of the total urban population, dominate in several districts. These districts tend to be isolated from each other and, apart from a wedge-shaped area which spreads out to part of the western city boundary, they tend to be located in the old inner city districts. In contrast the Protestants tend to live in the newer suburban areas.

Since 1969, when sectarian strife began in Northern Ireland, there have been significant population movements within the city. Figure 9.16 illustrates a typical demarcation line between Protestants and Roman Catholics, and in such streets near to the so-called Peace Line (dividing the Protestant Shankhill and Roman Catholic Falls Road areas, Figure 9.15) inhabitants have been forced to move out, and their houses have become bricked up or demolished. Furthermore, Protestants living in former Roman Catholic areas have moved out into Protestant areas, and Roman Catholics living in Protestant areas have likewise moved into Roman Catholic areas. This has led to

an even greater polarising of the two communities thereby adding to the problems of the city. It is estimated that between 1969 and 1973, 6000 families moved out of one area into another. Recent estimates also suggest that between 1969 and 1981 over 60 000 people moved either out of Northern Ireland altogether or to new districts within their own communities.

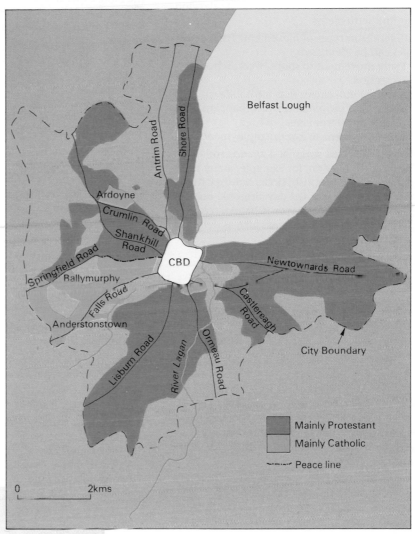

Figure 9.15 Population distribution in Belfast, Northern Ireland

Figure 9.16 Demolished houses helping to form a barrier in the Shankhill and Falls Road areas

TEN TRANSPORT

○ PROBLEMS

Problems associated with transport arise because of:

- A need for an efficient transport system to link economic activities, to link social amenities, to develop the full use of the land and to develop and link settlements.

- Differences in types of movement. Three main types can be identified:
  1 Daily movement to shops, work, school, recreation.
  2 Seasonal movement (e.g. for holidays).
  3 Permanent movement, which happens when people move from areas of high unemployment to low unemployment.

- Uneven daily and seasonal demands and uses of transport. In London, for example, many trains are needed at peak (rush) hours but they then lie idle for the rest of the day. Seasonal demand for summer flights and cross-Channel ferries in summer also create problems, such as delays to passengers (Figure 10.28).

- Transport is a major user of energy.

% of Britain's annual energy consumption

	1976	1986
All transport	22	28
Motor vehicles	17	22
Air transport	3	4
Rail	1	1
Water	1	1

Added to this oil forms 99% of the energy used by transport. What will happen when our reserves of oil are exhausted, or the price continues to rise?

- Constantly rising costs, leading to more expensive food and more expensive raw materials, and more expensive finished products, take up a larger proportion of the family's budget.

- Increasing conflict between different types of transport (especially car and rail).

- Growth of conservation groups such as Friends of the Earth and Greenpeace who try to:
  1 Reduce the noise and fumes caused by traffic.
  2 Reduce the amount of land threatened by future motorway and airport extensions.
  3 Oppose the wholesale reshaping of towns to suit the motorist.

- Transport, by using fossil fuels, is a major pollutant of the atmosphere. Car exhausts in particular are a major cause of acid rain and a contribution factor to the Greenhouse Effect (p114).

- Declining transport services in rural areas.

- A fall in world trade which particularly affects water and air transport.

Problems of time, distance and cost

Until fairly recently there was a close correlation between time, distance and cost. This meant that the further you travelled, the longer it took and the more expensive it became. This need not necessarily apply today. For example, a London family having a one-week holiday might have gone to:

1 Brighton or Margate (95 km) in the nineteenth century.
2 Devon and Cornwall (450 km to Penzance) in the 1950s.
3 The Costa Brava (1500 km) in the 1970s.
4 Miami, Florida (8000 km) in the 1990s.

Yet the cost of the journey and time taken need not necessarily have been any greater.

The radial charts in Figure 10.1 give a comparison between two families. Look at these charts and explain:

1 Why does Mr Jones have further to travel to work? And why might he take less time to get to work than Mr Smith?
2 Why is there a good correlation between time and distance for both of them when they visit the National Park?
3 Why can Mr Smith reach the regional shopping centre faster than can Mr Jones despite his living further away?

Can you now give reasons why time, distance and cost are important to the following:

1 Commuters
2 Holidaymakers
3 An industry needing raw materials
4 A new leisure centre
5 A fresh fruit farmer
6 A new shopping centre manager
7 A long distance lorry driver?

Figure 10.1 Time-distance comparison

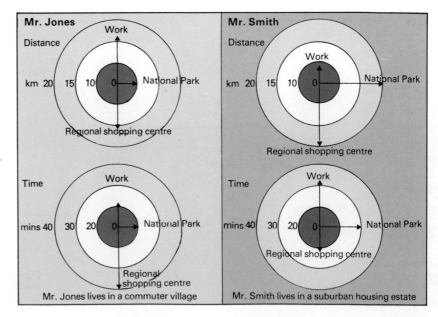

Transport in competition

The continual increase in both passenger and freight traffic is shown in Figure 10.2, and the relative changes in the importance of road and rail transport in Figure 10.3. Figure 10.4 illustrates the type of transport used by people in Britain to get to and from work, and Figure 10.5 the advantages and disadvantages of each of the main forms of transport.

Figure 10.3 Changes in road and rail transport 1960-1986

	1960	1975	1986
Rail routes, passengers (hundreds km)	222	144	143
Length of motorways (hundreds km)	1.5	20	30
Length of other main roads (hundreds km)	450	463	473
Open rail stations	4877	2358	2405
Number of cars (millions)	5.5	14.8	17.0
Number of driving licences (millions)	10.0	17.5	21.7

Figure 10.2 Movement of passengers and freight according to type of transport

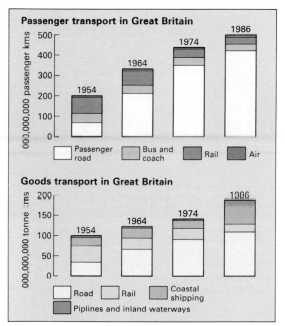

Figure 10.4 Modes of transport — to and from work

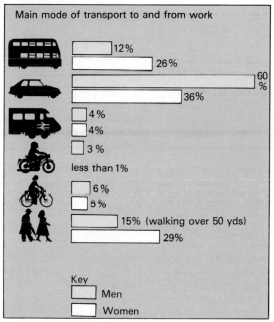

Figure 10.5 Types of transport — advantages and disadvantages

	Car - Lorry	Train	Air	Water
Speed/Time	Fast over short distances and on motorways	Fast over longer distances	Fastest over longest distances	Slowest
Distance/Costs	Cheapest over shortest distances	Relatively cheaper over longer distances with bulk goods	Relatively cheaper over long distances with light goods	Cheapest
Running Costs	High costs of building new roads and repairing older ones. Lorries relatively cheap	High cost of maintaining track, new signalling, and new trains	Large airports —expensive use of land. High cost of airports	High cost of port dues and large specialised ships
Number of routes	Numerous — and at differing levels (motorways to minor roads)	Mainly limited to Inter-City passengers and freight	Few internal airports	Few coastal ports. Little inland traffic
Congestion	Heavy in towns on major motorways. Peaks daily and seasonal	No track congestion — limited to commuter trains	Very little	Very little
Weather	Fog and ice cause accidents. Snow causes blockages	Virtually unaffected	Fog grounds planes. Icing	Storms affect coasts
Volume of freight	Small tonnage	Greater tonnage. Heavier bulk	Limited to light, high value and perishable goods	Heavy, bulky goods
Passengers	3-4 adults	Several hundred	Up to 200 on internal flights	Very few passengers
Convenience	Door-to-door	Town to town	City to city	Poor
Comfort	Strain for drivers	Good over medium distance	Good over long distance	Good
Pollution	Noise and air pollution acid rain, Greenhouse Effect	Noise pollution limited to narrow belts	High noise pollution. Some air pollution	Virtually none

○ CITY TRANSPORT

Some problems

Congestion caused by private cars, service lorries and public transport can cause havoc in cities (Figure 10.16).

Why do city centres experience congestion?

- Routes from suburbs and surrounding towns often converge here
- Older cities have unplanned road systems built before the introduction of cars and lorries. Many roads are too narrow to accommodate todays volume of traffic
- Commuters working in the CBD create two rush hour peaks each week-day.
- Lack of parking spaces for the commuter and shopper.
- Delays caused by buses and unloading delivery lorries.
- Road works, often to repair underground utilities or to try to improve traffic flows, increase traffic jams.

Problems of traffic in cities are increasing. It is estimated that car ownership will increase by 30%; traffic in cities by 40% and the time taken for a journey 50% by the year 2025. Rush hours are lasting longer — in some cities even all day. One recent report claimed that as a nation the cost of lost working time and delays in deliveries costs us £15 billion a year.

Much attention is now being focused upon the detrimental effect of traffic on our health and the environment. Transport creates noise and visual pollution and can shake and damage nearby buildings. Car exhausts emit fumes which may cause respiratory illnesses as well as being a major contributary factor to acid rain and the Greenhouse Effect (pages 114–115).

Lead pollution from engine exhaust can lead to brain damage and mental retardation. An acceptable level is two micrograms. In a survey taken in Leeds it was shown that the lead level was 1.9 micrograms on the ring road, 3.2 in City Square, and 18.9 in Westgate Underpass. The acceptable level for carbon monoxide is 50 parts per million, yet Westgate Underpass varied between 60 to 100 parts.

Because of heavier traffic in the city accidents occur more frequently between cars, other forms of transport and pedestrians. In addition the amount of land given over to roads and car parks means less space in the city.

Urban motorways — a solution or a problem?

Urban motorways (Figure 10.7) are also making us wonder if towns are designed for cars or for people. Some people think that urban motorways are a

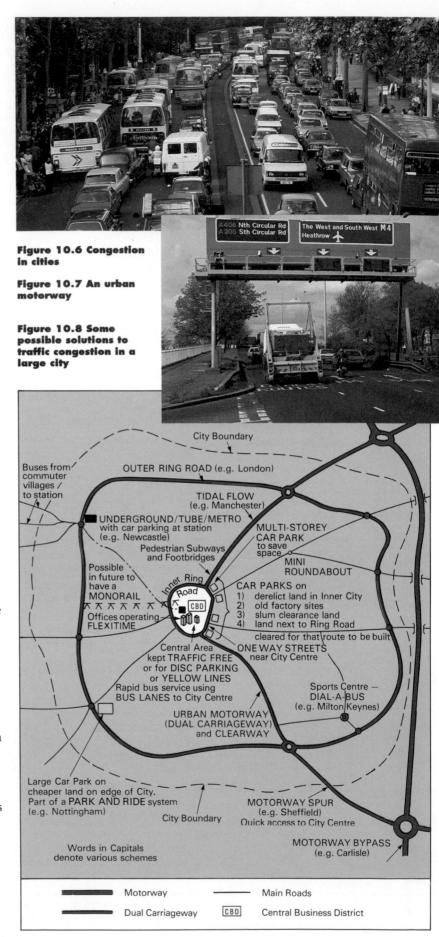

Figure 10.6 Congestion in cities

Figure 10.7 An urban motorway

Figure 10.8 Some possible solutions to traffic congestion in a large city

blessing because they help the flow of traffic, they make driving easier, they reduce congestion in inner city areas, and they reduce accidents by segregating cars from pedestrians. Other people think, on the other hand, that they take up valuable land, their construction results in the demolition of buildings, they are expensive to construct, they increase noise and air pollution to residents living nearby, and they devalue adjacent housing.

Some solutions

Figure 10.8 illustrates twenty different ways in which the problem of traffic congestion in towns might be solved. These schemes vary from the relatively cheap disc parking to the construction of an expensive underground system. Which of these schemes have been tried in your local town or city? How effective do you think they have been? Which other schemes would you introduce if you were a planner? Perhaps the information below on four schemes may help you to make your decision.

Bus lanes The aim of this scheme is to separate cars and buses by providing an inside lane just for buses. Bus lanes operate either all day or, for example, from Monday to Friday between 0730 and 0930 hours.

Park and ride schemes try to limit the number of cars entering the CBD by providing large car parks on relatively cheap land on the edges of urban areas, and then running buses at low prices from these car parks into the CBD. Ideally this should reduce delays, congestion, noise, fumes and accidents in the centre but unfortunately the modern motorist prefers to wait in queues of traffic, trying to get as near to work and the shops as possible.

A tidal (contra) flow scheme operates in two parts of Manchester. A five-lane urban motorway was built with traffic lights at short distances above and along its length. In the morning at least three lanes are open for traffic going into town, whereas at night at least three lanes are open to motorists leaving Manchester. Traffic flows can be reversed to suit the direction of maximum flows (Figure 10.10).

The Metro was Britain's first ever fully integrated public transport system linking buses with 'supertrams'. Originally known as a 'rapid transit system' (Figure 10.9), the first part of what is now called Metro was opened in Newcastle in 1980. These special 'supertrams' travel for more than 55 km both overground (mainly linking the suburbs, coastal and commuter settlements) and underground (inner city and city centre areas). Much of the track used was formerly part of a British Rail system. Of the 46 stations, 15 are new (7 of which are underground) and the remainder have been modernised with special facilities for the elderly and disabled.

Buses link with several Metro stations (tickets can be used on either form of transport) while other stations have free car parking facilities. Its advantages include speed, comfort and relative cheapness, together with cleanliness and the fact that it removes travellers from previously congested main roads and bridges over the River Tyne.

The Metro won export orders as similar rapid transport systems have been built in Hong Kong and Singapore. In 1990 a planned extension to Newcastle airport was awaiting final approval, while a feasibility study was being undertaken with the aim of linking Washington New Town and Sunderland to the network.

Light railway systems

The London Docklands Development Corporation built the Docklands Light Railway at the heart of their development scheme (Figure 10.11). Opened in 1987, it is being extended to the City to cope with the increased traffic generated by the Canary Wharf development in the Isle of Dogs Enterprise Zone (page 124). It provides a clean, efficient public transport system which can compete with the private motorist.

Manchester has completed its study of a similar light rail system and work began on its 100 km tram-like scheme in late 1989. 'Super-trams' will use overhead electricity supplies and, wherever possible, existing wide roads. Birmingham, Bristol, Sheffield, Cardiff, Edinburgh, Portsmouth, Nottingham and Leeds have also been linked with possible future cost-effective schemes aimed at reducing pressure on their road systems.

Figure 10.9 The Tyne and Wear Metro (bottom left)

Figure 10.10 Tidal flow system in operation (top)

Figure 10.11 The London Docklands Light Railway (bottom right)

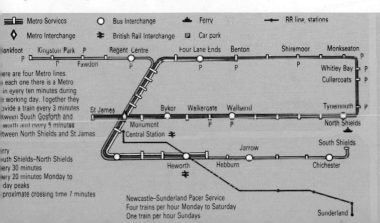

Metro Services | O Bus Interchange | Ferry | RR line, stations
Metro Interchange | British Rail Interchange | P Car park

Bankfoot | Kingston Park P | Regent Centre | Four Lane Ends | Benton | Shiremoor | Monkseaton
Fawdon | Whitley Bay P
Cullercoats P

There are four Metro lines. On each one there is a Metro every ten minutes during the working day. Together they provide a train every 3 minutes between South Gosforth and Monument and every 5 minutes between North Shields and St James

St James | Byker | Walkergate | Wallsend | Tynemouth P
Monument | North Shields P
Central Station

Ferry South Shields–North Shields every 30 minutes every 20 minutes Monday to day peaks approximate crossing time 7 minutes

Jarrow | South Shields
Heworth | Hebburn | Chichester

Newcastle–Sunderland Pacer Service Four trains per hour Monday to Saturday One train per hour Sundays

Sunderland

⊙ ACCESSIBILITY

Figure 10.12 shows Britain's completed motorways, and some of its proposed, new motorways. Notice how they:

- Link up major conurbations.
- Bypass major conurbations and cities.
- Link industrial areas with major ports.
- Link up conurbations with National Parks (though not passing through them) and other tourist areas.
- Avoid highland areas.
- Avoid the more rural areas.
- Radiate outwards from London.

Notice that they also:

- Make journeys faster for the tourist, the long-distance lorry driver and even the commuter, due to constant high speeds.
- Allow larger and therefore fewer lorries to operate.
- Reduce accidents by having no oncoming traffic, no severe bends and no road junctions.
- Attract new industries, especially at interchange points.

But remember too that motorways:

- Take up large areas of land (both urban and farmland). A one-kilometre stretch of three-lane motorway, for example, takes up to 16 hectares.
- Have high construction and maintenance costs.
- Cause heavy delays in times of maintenance.
- Cause congestion at peak times at ends of motorways.
- May produce serious pile-ups in times of extreme weather conditions (Figure 2.23).

The M25 orbital road

This motorway, completed in 1986, encircles London linking motorways and main roads from other parts of Britain (Figure 10.13). It was built to try to:

- Make it easier to drive from one side of London to the other without having to pass through the city itself.
- Reduce the volume of traffic, especially heavy lorries and coaches, entering Central London. It was hoped that this would reduce the amount of noise and air pollution as well as congestion.
- Relieve the overcrowded North and South Circular (outer) Ring roads.
- Link motorways converging on the capital.
- Link up the four London airports at Heathrow, Gatwick, Luton and Stanstead.

When the motorway was planned it was believed that its three lanes could carry the predicted 80 000 vehicles a day. To reduce the objections of local residents and conservationists the route meandered around villages and small towns, was in part landscaped and even, between the M11 and the A121, had bridges and underpasses to allow the migration of deer.

The M25 has confirmed the view that new roads attract more traffic which causes an increase in the amount of congestion and pollution. The 160 000 vehicles per day cause many accidents and lengthy hold-ups — the record jam to date is a 35 km three lane standstill. Already a fourth lane has been added (the roadworks adding to the delays) on the Heathrow to Gatwick section. Another early bottleneck was at the Dartford Tunnel under the River Thames. The new road bridge, which is being built, will be paid for by money raised from the collection of tolls. It has already been suggested that a new orbital road, further out from London than the M25 be built to encircle the capital.

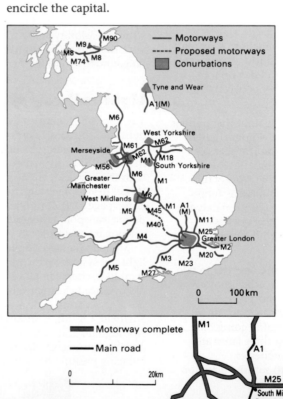

Figure 10.12 The motorways of Britain

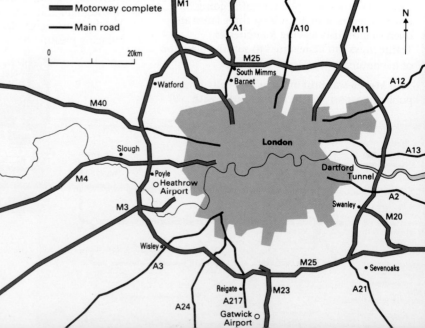

Figure 10.13 The M25 and London's motorways

Declining services and accessibility of rural areas

Rail services even at their height in the 1930s only served selected rural areas. In the 1960s most of these stations were either closed down (Figure 10.14) or left unmanned. Bus services have also been drastically cut back. The reduction in primary bus services (defined as more than four buses a day) is not compensated for by the small increase in secondary bus services (e.g. one bus per week on market days).

Rural areas are faced with such problems as:

- Do buses run at convenient times for work, school or shopping?
- Is there a Sunday service?
- Do buses link up with recreational amenities and welfare services?
- The cost of maintaining school buses.
- The increased cost of petrol which in turn causes rising fares.
- Declining mobile services (e.g. library vans, travelling shops).

Look at Figure 10.15 which shows part of a bus timetable for the Isle of Arran. How many buses run on a normal Tuesday, Friday and Saturday? What problems do you think this poses to local residents?

What the future might be for rural services:

- A continual decline in rural services as costs increase (Figure 10.16).
- The use of the postal mini-bus service where isolated families could have regular, cheap access to nearby towns for shopping and visiting, whereby their fares could subsidise the mail. Yet in the Scottish Highlands, instead of the anticipated 500 services by 1981, by 1988 the peak of 100 had declined to 70. A similar service in the Isle of Skye closed after carrying only two passengers in the whole of 1980.
- The continuing development of the key settlement policy where a mini-bus travels through several small villages collecting passengers and taking them to a 'key settlement' which has a regular bus service to the larger nearby towns.

Inward, Monday to Saturday

	SE,SS	SO,SH	MFS	FO
Pirnmill	8.00am	9.15am	2.45pm	5.50pm
Catacol	8.10am	9.25am	2.55pm	6.00pm
Lochranza	8.15am	9.30am	3.00pm	6.05pm
Corrie	8.40am	9.55am	3.25pm	6.30pm
Brodick	9.00am	10.15am	3.45pm	6.50pm

Outward, Monday to Saturday

	MFS		FO,SO
Brodick	10.40am	4.15pm	7.00pm
Corrie	11.00am	4.35pm	7.20pm
Lochranza	11.25am	5.00pm	7.45pm
Catacol	11.30am	5.05pm	7.50pm
Pirnmill	11.40am	5.15pm	8.00pm

SE	Saturdays excepted	SO	Saturdays only
SS	School Session only	FO	Fridays only
SH	School Holidays	MFS	Monday, Friday, Saturdays

No Sunday Service

Figure 10.15 Rural bus timetable for the Isle of Arran

Figure 10.16 Rural transport

Figure 10.14 A disused railway station, Great Longstore, Peak District

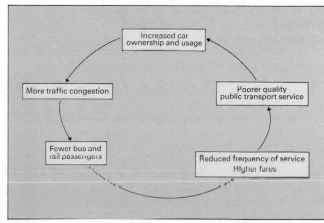

Figure 10.17 Rural accessibility

Problems facing British Rail in the early 1990s

These problems include:

- Expensive and ageing track (much of which is freight lines or in sidings) which needs maintenance and renewal.

- Much of the rolling stock — locomotives, carrriages and wagons — was built in the late 1960s and 70s and needs replacing.

- Competition from other forms of transport (Figure 10.5) including cars and coaches (for passenger traffic and especially commuters in SE England); lorries (freight traffic) over relatively short distances; and planes (air freight) over longer distances. In 1954 freight trains carried 294 million tonnes, in 1986 only 157 million tonnes.

	1976	1986
locomotives	3689	2441
carriages	17 111	13 677
wagons	205 400	48 400

- An unpredicted increase in both Inter City and South-east England commuters has found British Rail short of stock.

- British Rail has had the lowest investment per train/km compared with other rail services in Western Europe. This decline in investment began in the early 1970s and was only reversed (slowly) after 1984.

- Government subsidies were withdrawn after April 1988. British Rail must, in future, make a profit.

- Under-use of stock, except at peak times, especially in South-east England.

- Questions of safety e.g. one-man trains; staff shortages; maintenance of track and signalling; and vandalism.

- Union and management disagreements.

- A poor public image

How is British Rail trying to attract more freight and passengers?

Freight

Computerised signalling and wagon control and the introduction of freightliners are speeding up services. Freightliners take containers made to internationally agreed sizes to fit specialised ships, trains and lorries. Manufacturers load and seal the containers which can be moved rapidly saving time, labour and haulage costs as well as reducing theft and damage. Specialist wagons are used to carry bulk materials, for example coal, cement and nuclear waste. The Government give customers grants for freight to be carried by rail where this will benefit the environment.

Passenger comfort

A British rail survey in 1989 showed that passengers regarded comfort and service to be their top priorities. All Inter-City carriages are now air-conditioned (compared with only 46% in 1976). Many new and more comfortable coaches are being built while staff have been trained to be more helpful. Pullman trains are to be reintroduced in greater numbers.

West Coast Main Line (WCML)

The tilting Advanced Passenger Train (APT), introduced in December 1981, ran into major technological difficulties. It was designed to reach speeds of 250 km per hour (155 mph) and to negotiate tighter bends and steeper inclines than existing locomotives. New trials began on a revised model in mid-1984 with the coaches still tilting, but drawn by a lightweight, streamlined locomotive which will not exceed 225 km per hour (140 mph) — hence its name, 'Intercity 225'. It is hoped that 30 new locomotives will be ordered in 1990 to run from London to Glasgow and North-west England.

East Coast Main Line (ECML)

The Secretary of State for Transport approved, in mid-1984, a £306 million investment in the electrification of the ECML. Electrification is expected to reach York, Newcastle and Edinburgh by May 1991. The entire route will be controlled from only seven modern signalling centres. Curves are being straightened and bridges and stations rebuilt.

Estimates suggest the scheme should create 3000 jobs. Although there are no plans to increase train speeds over the existing 200 km per hour (125 mph), the 31 proposed new Electra locomotives have the ability to reach 225 km per hour (140 mph).

These new high speed electra locomotives should be easier to maintain and service than the present 125 diesel engines (Figure 10.18). Once electrification has been completed the journey from London should only take two and a half hours to Newcastle and four hours to Edinburgh (Compare the present times on Figure 10.19). Figure 10.20 shows other electrification schemes in progress in 1990.

Figure 10.18 New Class 91 locomotive

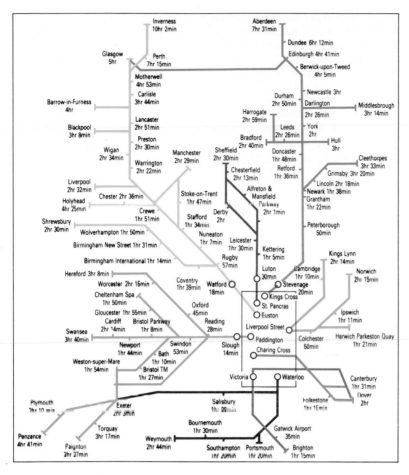

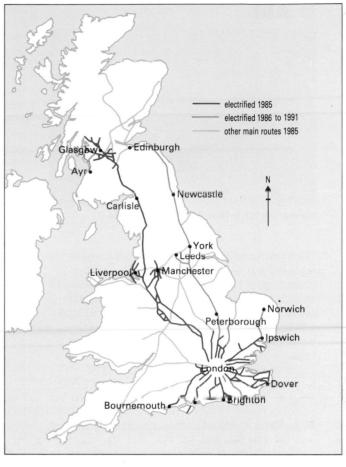

**Figure 10.19
A topological map to show British Rail's major routes with the fastest travel time from London (left)**

Figure 10.20 The electrification of British Rail (right)

Figure 10.22 A proposed new passenger train for travel through the Channel Tunnel

Channel Fixed Link (CFL)

The British and French governments agreed, in January 1986, to accept a scheme which involved building two rail tunnels. Each would have a diameter of 7.3 m, linked by a central service tunnel, with a diameter of 4.5 m bored in advance to overcome geological problems. The tunnels are to connect Cheriton (north west of Folkestone) and Frethun (south west of Calais). Of the 50 km of tunnel, 37 km will be underwater. Hopes are for the first shuttle trains to be running by 1993. This scheme had political advantages in that it had relatively low costs (compared with other schemes), was paid for by private investors, should have comparatively few technological risks, and could provide as many as 5000 British jobs on the tunnel construction and another 25 000 in associated industries (e.g. concrete tunnel linings, and tunnel boring equipment). As yet no decision has been made regarding which high speed train (expected to travel through the tunnel at 160 km per hour (100 mph)) will be used. Will it be France's TGV (Train à Grande Vitesse) or Britain's new Electra? (Figure 10.22).

The Channel Tunnel Link

Four options were investigated by British Rail as to the best route to link London (King's Cross) and Folkestone. The preferred option was to cost £1.2 billion. However this route was the most environmentally sensitive as well affecting many wealthy and influential residents who lived in or near its path. As a result of an organised opposition by conservationists and residents the chosen route was one which was to cost £1.7 billion. This route was less environmentally damaging and the people it affected had less influence. While residents of Kent were fighting to **avoid** the tunnel link being built near to them, inhabitants of Amiens in France were equally annoyed — though in their case it was because they were **not** to be on the chosen route!

Figure 10.21 The Channel Tunnel

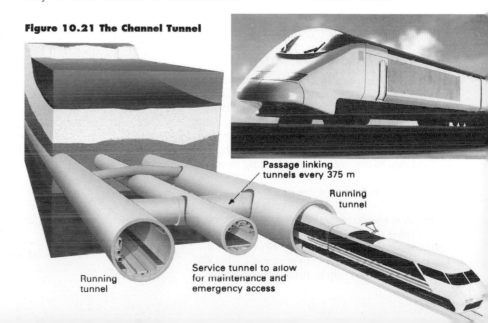

Passage linking tunnels every 375 m

Running tunnel

Running tunnel

Service tunnel to allow for maintenance and emergency access

○ AIR

Figure 10.23 British Airways Concorde

With the Anglo-French Concorde, Britain now leads the way with a fast, comfortable, reliable plane (Figure 10.23). In 1984 Concorde earned £12 million for British Airways. The plane is usually full at peak periods on its London-New York and London-Washington-Miami routes. Although having to fly subsonic overland, its supersonic capacity for crossing the Atlantic in 3½ hours leaves its passengers free from travel fatigue. Concorde is undertaking over 200 charters a year ranging from the 'out and back' day visit to such places as Egypt, to longer flights to Sydney and Hong Kong. Concorde's life is expected to last well into the 21st century.

Figure 10.26 gives the number of passengers who passed through Britain's major passenger airports in 1988. Why do you think that Heathrow is so important? In what ways does Gatwick take some of the pressure from Heathrow? What is the major difference in the types of flight between the two airports? Why do airways and many air passengers want a third London airport to be built?

London Airport is also a major freight outlet. The goods carried are of a high value in relation to size and weight (e.g. watches, jewellery, papers) or they are perishable (e.g. fresh fruit and vegetables). The major single item is mail. Heathrow now handles more goods in value than any British sea port.

A third airport for London

As the estimated number of passengers and amount of freight continue to grow, proposals have been made since the late 1960s for a third London airport. Heathrow has little further room for expansion, and it already has planes landing every two minutes in daytime (night flights are limited due to the noise levels affecting local residents).

Gatwick has become even more congested, especially at peak holiday weekends in the summer. It has no second runway in the event of an accident. The first favoured site for London's third airport was Stansted to the North-east of London. Following strong opposition to this site, a committee was set up to study other possible

sites. Of these, Maplin (a coastal area needing to be reclaimed from the sea) was first chosen and then rejected. The ideal requirements for any new airport are shown in Figure 10.27. In 1985 the government approved Stansted. Its capacity increased from 2 million (only half a million of this was used) in 1984 to 8 million in 1990. Stansted has space, is adjacent to a mainline railway and the M11, is away from built up areas and could create many local jobs. However future growth is threatened by opposition by conservation groups, regional authorities who see it promoting jobs in the south-east of the country at the expense of the north and west, and residents in the south-east who realise most flights will still have to cross London and the flightpaths at Heathrow and Gatwick.

Figure 10.24 The location of Britain's airports

Figure 10.25 Britain's airports according to category

Categories of British Airports

Category	Description
A	'Gateway International Airports'. These would provide a wide range and frequency of international services, including inter-continental services, and a full range of domestic services.
B	'Regional Airports' These would cater for the main air traffic demands of the regions outside the south-east. They would have a network of short-range international services and domestic services which would include links to gateway international airports.
C	'Local Airports' These would provide a limited number of services flown by small aircraft to cater for local needs, including feeder services to gateway international airports.
D	'General Aviation Aerodromes' These would be concerned with general aviation (business and leisure flying).

Leading passenger airports			
	% UK total 1976	1976(millions)	1988(millions)
Heathrow	49.9	23.2	37.5
Gatwick	12.3	5.7	20.6
Manchester	5.9	2.8	10.0
Glasgow	4.3	2.0	3.6
Luton	3.9	1.8	2.7
Birmingham	2.6	1.6	2.8
40 others	21.1	9.5	48.8
Total	100.0	46.6	126.0
	%scheduled fligts 1976	% chartered flights 1976	% scheduled flights 1984	% chartered flights 1984
Heathrow	100	0	100	0
Gatwick	28	72	41	59

Figure 10.26 Passenger transport through British airports

Figure 10.27 The ideal site for an airport

Figure 10.28 Passenger congestion at Gatwick Airport

Airport and airspace congestion. Problems for the 1990s

Delays for passengers at many British airports, especially at Gatwick, hit the headlines during most weekends in the summers of 1988 and 1989. (Figure 10.28).

Although mainly due to strikes by overseas air traffic controllers and engineers, this was not the major underlying problem. Scheduled international traffic handled by British airports increased by over 50% and domestic traffic by 80% during the 1980s. This had led to congestion at, and in getting to, airports and increasing competition for airspace. The Civil Aviation Authority (CAA) has estimated that the 62 million passengers who used the four airports in the London area in 1988 will increase to 123 million by the end of the century. New computers and an increase in airspace are not expected until the mid-1990s. Until then, passengers can expect delays on the ground and reduced safety margins in the air.

As Heathrow and Gatwick are already almost at full capacity, what are some of the options? Both airports could increase their number of off-peak flights but this would mean more flights during the night which is not favoured by passengers or local residents. A fifth terminal could be added at Heathrow but this would add to congestion. The capacity of Luton could be increased and that at Stansted utilised, (see opposite) but the CAA believe that the air would be less safe and London noisier if the development was to the north of the capital. A new airport could be built on reclaimed land on the Maplin Sands in the Thames estuary — a site rejected on environmental and economic grounds in the 1970s. In 1989 an all party group of politicians, supported by airline pilots, recommended a second runway at Gatwick. It was immediately objected to by local residents and environmentalists.

The 'extra runway' is a classic example of the NIMBY syndrome — it is accepted as essential but 'Not In My Back Yard'. The runway is a major transport issue for the 1990s with the safety and convenience of air travellers against the quality of life of local residents and the protection of the environment.

Good weather with limited days of fog, snow and high winds

Long way from other airports to avoid traffic control problems

Near motorway and rail link, yet not too far from urban areas (1½ hours or 80km)

Urban areas to west so that prevailing winds blow fumes and noise away

Not too near to large urban areas for safety reasons and less noise and air pollution

Poor quality farmland

Large areas of flat land for terminal buildings and runways

Land of low scenic value
Land lacking in wildlife

Prevailing S.W. winds

Runway 3km long

⊙ WATER

Many rapid changes have occurred recently in British ports. These have included:

■ The increase in ship size which has meant that wider, deeper and more sheltered estuaries are necessary.

■ A decrease in world trade. This has led to both a decrease in the number of ships and the number of ports needed.

■ The growth of bulk-handling ports (e.g. oil at Milford Haven and iron ore at Port Talbot) and the growth of specialised handling ports (e.g. fruit in London, grain at Southampton).

■ The development of roll on/roll off methods (Ro-Ro) which are replacing the traditional crane handling methods known as break-bulk which were labour intensive. The speed with which cargo is unloaded and loaded is essential, as the longer the ship is in dock the more money is lost. The Ro-Ro method has been in use for some time for continental passenger traffic.

■ The so-called container revolution has speeded up the loading and unloading of cargo. The first container port was at Felixstowe (1967) but more have been developed, especially in the South and East, because of this area's close links with the EC (Figure 10.30). Some of the latest container ships can hold upwards of 4000 containers (Figure 10.31). This mode of cargo handling is closely linked with British Rail and road transport.

■ A loss of jobs within the docks due to increased containerisation and fewer, even if larger, ships. The older, largest ports of London and Liverpool have suffered most.

■ Changing overseas markets and trade routes. In the nineteenth century such west coast ports as Bristol, Liverpool, Manchester and Glasgow thrived on the colonial and American trade. Even in 1960 (Figure 10.33) London and Liverpool together handled 59% of British

trade in value. This trade has decreased while the trade handled by ports in the South and East has grown since Britain's entry into the EC. Compare the rank order of ports in 1960 with that of 1984.

■ Increased seasonal pressures of holiday makers on cross-Channel ports especially at Dover, (which has 6.8 million passengers a year), Folkestone (1.6 million), Harwich (1.5 million) and Southampton (1.1 million).

Figure 10.30 The location of Britain's container ports

British Rail
● Containerports
● Planned 'Freightliner' Terminals
● 'Freightliner' Terminals

Figure 10.31 Container ship loading at Felixstowe

Figure 10.29 Tilbury container port

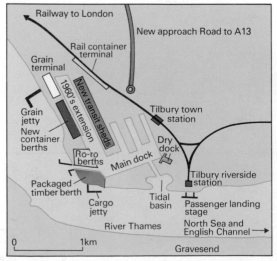

- Introduction of new forms of transport such as the Hovercraft (Figure 10.32). It is faster than other ships (55-60 knots), can travel on land and sea, (as it floats on a cushion of air), and it does not need expensive docks and harbours, since it can operate from an ordinary beach.

- A slight increase in the use of inland waterways as a tourist attraction. They also provide a cheap method of transporting bulky, non-perishable goods at low value per weight. Nevertheless there has been an overall decline in Britain in moving freight, such as coal, coke, and liquid fuels.

Felixstowe: a modern expanding port

From a near derelict site in 1950, Felixstowe is now Britain's premier container port. This is due to:

- Its being a deep water port capable of handling large vessels.

- Being sited on the coast, thus avoiding time wasting journeys up river estuaries.

- Being on the major trade route between Britain and both the EC and Scandinavia.

- Its modern equipment, and its efforts to gain container traffic. In 1986 a fourth container terminal was opened, and applications were made to purchase Trimley Marshes for a fifth terminal. The major European linked container ports are Rotterdam and Zeebrugge.

- The development of Ro-Ro facilities. These help speed up the turn-around of the ship (any merchant vessel in dock is losing money).

- Good industrial relations (it has only one union) which has earned the port a reputation for being efficient and reliable.

- Good road links with its hinterland which pass through mainly non-urban land and so are less congested than the approaches to other British ports.

London: an old declining port

The reasons for the decline of London as a major port include:

- The older traditional break-bulk method by cranes which accounts for lost time and increased labour charges.

Figure 10.32 Hovercraft used on cross-Channel routes

- Problems caused from trying to improve road links through the built-up hinterland of Greater London.

- The River Thames is too shallow and narrow for larger vessels.

- London being sited inland means a long, slow journey from the sea. Many docks in London have closed as the outport of Tilbury has increased in importance (Figure 10.29).

- Colonial trade and links with Africa and Australasia have gradually declined since the turn of the century.

- Poor industrial relations have led to a loss of trade to rival ports.

- Out-of-date equipment.

Figure 10.33 Trade (by value) through Britain's major ports

Figure 10.34 Average annual percentage change in traffic, 1968-86

	Value (£millions)		% of total	
	1960	1984	1960	1984
London	6872.4	10 712.5	36	10.9
Liverpool	4192.3	4022.9	23	4.0
Hull	2152.7	3592.3	6	3.7
Manchester	-	1447.0	5	1.5
Southampton	4783.8	7846.6	4	8.0
Clyde		1441.0	4	1.3
Dover	4553.9	18 092.0	2	18.4
Harwich	2541.2	5310.6	2	5.4
Felixstowe	3284.2	13 317.3	1	13.6
Immingham	1656.0	5436.0	1	5.5
Milford Haven	1671.3	2504.3	0	24.8
Others	18 345.5	24 416.2	16	24.8
Total	**50 051.2**	**98 139.5**	**100**	**100**

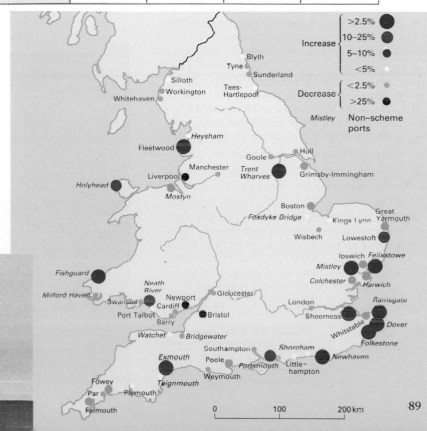

O HIERARCHIES

Figure 11.1 is a map of a city on which the traditional locations of four types of shopping areas are drawn. If a stylised diagram (Figure 11.2) is made, based on the data from the city map, it becomes immediately apparent that there exists a definite urban shopping hierarchy. Look now at the map of the city and notice the frequency and locations of each of the four shopping types.

1 Many small corner shops are usually in old inner city areas, though occasionally they can also be found in the outer suburbs (the village shop has a similar function).

2 Several small suburban parades made up of 5-20 shops and mostly located in large housing estates.

3 Two or three large shopping areas are found alongside main roads which lead into the city centre.

4 The major shopping area is situated in the city centre (CBD) and contains many large department stores and specialist shops.

The corner shop

Corner shops can still be found in non-redeveloped inner city areas and date from the nineteenth century when Victorian workers had little spare time (due to long hours of work) and limited mobility, since there were no cars or public transport. These shops served a small trade area (several streets) and were visited frequently (daily) as they sold many different foods and other necessities (Figure 11.3).

Despite being multi-functional, they are not very profitable today as they tend to be expensive through their lack of space for bulk buying. They also only keep a limited range and volume of stock because of their small floor area. As a result many have closed down due to competition from city centre shops and edge of city superstores or have been demolished in inner city redevelopment schemes. However, those still remaining provide useful services such as:

■ A place for locals to meet. This is important in areas with a high elderly population.

■ They sell low order or convenience goods such as bread, newspapers, sweets, milk, etc. which are needed daily.

■ They are easily accessible, being usually within walking distance. And because they are open for long and often irregular hours (e.g. Sunday mornings) they attract customers who have forgotten odd items while shopping in the supermarkets, or who receive unexpected guests.

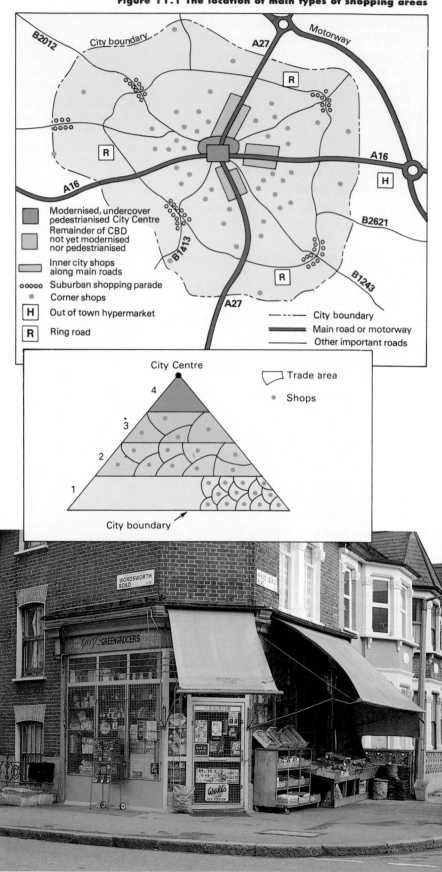

Figure 11.1 The location of main types of shopping areas

Modernised, undercover pedestrianised City Centre

Remainder of CBD not yet modernised nor pedestrianised

Inner city shops along main roads

ooooo Suburban shopping parade

• Corner shops

H Out of town hypermarket

R Ring road

— · — City boundary

— Main road or motorway

— Other important roads

City Centre

Trade area

• Shops

City boundary

Figure 11.2 An urban shopping hierarchy (middle)

Figure 11.3 A corner shop, North London

Suburban shopping parades

As cities expanded in the inter- and post-war years, large housing estates (both private and council) developed on the outskirts, and with them, a parade of several shops (Figure 11.4). These provide:

- A relatively large, yet local market, saving local residents time and money from having to travel into the town or city centre.

- Mainly low order/convenience goods which are needed daily, and can be bought from the small chain stores (e.g. Spar, VG, Co-op).

- Specialist shops such as chemists and butchers, and shops which supply non-essential goods such as a DIY shop, a launderette or a hairdressers.

- Shops which the shopper might visit two or three times a week.

Inner city main road shopping areas

These usually consist of a line of shops alongside a main road leading into the city centre (Figure 11.5) or sometimes at the junction of two main roads in an inner city area (Figure 11.6).

These linear shopping areas developed because of:

- Their advantage of having good accessibility which increases their trade area.

- Numerous drivers who stop and buy on impulse.

- Their advantage to the motorist in not having to find and pay for car parks in the city centre.

- The majority of the shops in these areas, selling mainly low order goods, are small supermarkets or branches of large national concerns.

- The growing number of discount warehouses, motor car salesrooms and DIY stores.

Figure 11.4 A surburban shopping parade

Figure 11.5 A shopping centre on an inner city main road, South London

Figure 11.6 Types of shops found in an inner city shopping area

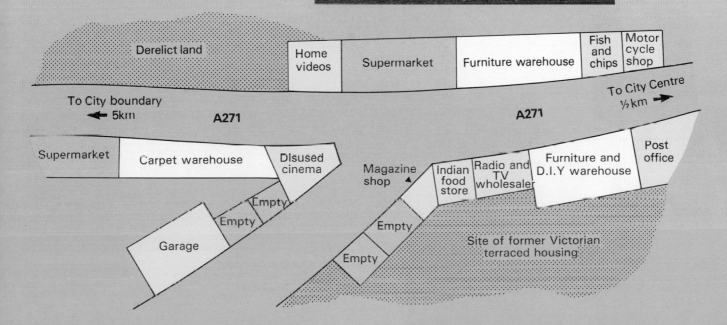

◉ CENTRAL BUSINESS DISTRICT

The main advantage of the city centre is its accessibility since it forms a junction of all the main roads leading into the city from the suburbs and surrounding towns and villages.

The chief characteristics of the CBD are:

■ The large variety of shops, the goods they sell and their large volume of stock.

■ The high land values which increase competition between shops for sales, and often lead to a development of two or three storeys to save space.

■ Large multi-functional department stores and nationwide supermarkets (Figure 11.7), both needing a rapid turnover of stock.

■ Many specialist shops selling high order durable goods, such as shoes, clothes, jewellery, electrical and furniture goods which generate high profit margins. These 'comparison' goods are bought less frequently, but customers like to be able to choose between various styles and prices.

■ The presence of commercial functions such as banks and building societies, as well as service functions such as travel agencies, cafes and hairdressers.

■ The cheaper priced supermarkets and specialist shops mean people will travel from a large trade area (beyond even the city boundary) but perhaps only weekly or monthly.

Precincts

Although the car has increased the mobility of shoppers and the trade of city centre shops, it has also led to such problems as parking, congestion, noise, air pollution and accidents. Precincts are traffic-free areas (Figure 11.8) created for the convenience, safety and comfort of the pedestrian, yet such under cover schemes as Eldon Square in Newcastle, have also increased the trade as well as improving the working conditions of shopkeepers. Other cities have partial traffic restrictions and still allow in certain traffic, such as delivery vans and buses.

A planning problem

One of the problems facing a local council is the decision whether to leave their town centre:

1 With open access to all traffic.
2 To limit access to just delivery vans and buses.
3 To make the town centre into a precinct.

What do you think would be the views of each of the following individuals: a local planner; an old-age pensioner; a city centre shopkeeper; a delivery van driver who works for a national supermarket chain; a traffic warden and a suburban housewife with a young family? Now give reasons for your answers.

Figure 11.7 A city centre shopping area — Oxford Street

Figure 11.8 A pedestrianised, covered shopping area — Frenchgate Shopping Centre, Doncaster

REGIONAL SHOPPING CENTRES

Eldon Square — Newcastle upon Tyne

Newcastle upon Tyne is the regional shopping centre for the North-east of England providing the shopper with some of the largest stores in the country within a compact and concentrated area. Eldon Square is located in the heart of the city and is one of Europe's largest enclosed centres. It consists of a network of enclosed pedestrian walkways (malls) which link a wide range of new shops and stores (Figure 11.9). As all the shops are under cover and have air conditioning the shopper is kept warm and is protected from the wind and rain. Because of this arrangement many of the traditional glass-fronted shops are able to present more open frontages onto the malls. The shopping scheme is based upon 'magnet' and specialist shops which 'attract' large numbers of shoppers from Tyneside, surrounding urban areas, and even Scandinavia.

Eldon Square has over 100 shops, six major stores, a market and a supermarket. They are all located in such a way as to encourage an even flow of pedestrians throughout the centre, eliminating bottlenecks and jostling crowds. Household names have decided to take the major store areas: Bainbridges (the largest John Lewis Partnership store outside London), Boots, Jacksons, W.H. Smith, Habitat and Mothercare. Also included are restaurants, pubs, cafes and a large modern recreation centre.

Although the complex is traffic free, the development went ahead in conjunction with four transport plans (Figure 11.10).

These four plans included:

1 A large modern bus station which was built under the complex to shorten the distance between public transport and the shops, and to provide an alternative to the car.
2 Two multi-storey car parks at either end of Eldon Square.
3 The building of an inner city urban motorway to keep through traffic away from the city centre.
4 The opening of the Metro rapid transit system (1980) and a linked Metro station (Monument, 1981).

The scheme was the result of successful co-operation between the city, the developers, the professional consultants, the transport executive, the shop owners and builders who managed to balance out the complex and, at times, conflicting interests of groups of people. When Eldon Square opened, the effect of the scheme became immediately felt. Pedestrian flows of over 8000 per hour (17 000 at peak times) were recorded along the central malls. One third of the shoppers were coming from beyond Tyneside including Edinburgh, Carlisle, Tees-side and Scandinavia and even shopkeepers from 100 miles away were affected. There was also an immediate, huge rise of sales in the 'magnet' shops and other shops.

Figure 11.9 Eldon Square shopping centre, Newcastle upon Tyne

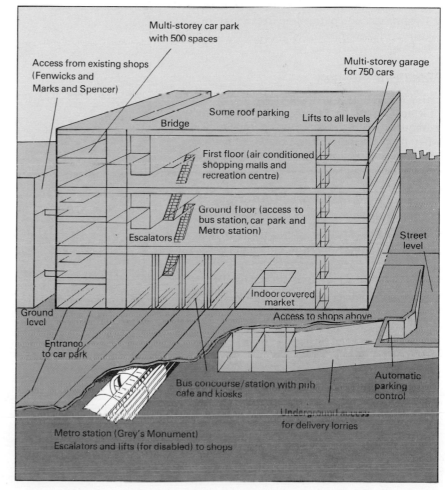

Figure 11.10 Eldon Square development scheme

Multi-storey car park with 500 spaces

Access from existing shops (Fenwicks and Marks and Spencer)

Bridge

Some roof parking

Lifts to all levels

Multi-storey garage for 750 cars

First floor (air conditioned shopping malls and recreation centre)

Ground floor (access to bus station, car park and Metro station)

Escalators

Street level

Indoor covered market

Access to shops above

Ground level

Entrance to car park

Bus concourse/station with pub cafe and kiosks

Automatic parking control

Underground access for delivery lorries

Metro station (Grey's Monument) Escalators and lifts (for disabled) to shops

○ CHANGING PATTERNS

In recent years there have been some notable changes in people's shopping habits and in the growth and decline of types of shops. These changes are given below:

The increased mobility of shoppers.

Due to more and more car owners (which includes the two-car, suburban, commuter-village family) people will now:
1 Travel further to shop.
2 Visit shops with a wider range and volume of stock.
3 Do more bulk buying.

Monthly pay packets

Now that more people are paid monthly it is easier to bulk buy once a month at a large supermarket or superstore. Shoppers will tend to bulk buy in the CBD or edge of city shopping centre and then use their local shops just for buying forgotten items, loss leaders and daily, low-order goods.

People shop less frequently

This is partly due to:
1 The increasing number of housewives in full-time employment, who have less time to shop.
2 The introduction of the deep freeze, and the growth of convenience foods (e.g. frozen, tinned foods).

Late night shopping

This partly results from the increase in the number of women in full-time employment. Friday night is frequently chosen since this is normally the day when people paid by the week receive their wages. Edge of city shopping centres may stay open until late on most nights.

The decline and closure of the village and corner shops

These shops have begun to close because of competition from city-centre shops, and because local residents have moved away from their home areas as a result of becoming commuters (thereby reducing shopping at the village shop). Inner city redevelopment schemes have also been a cause in the decline of the corner shop.

Discount warehouses and mail order firms

Both these outlets cater for the shopper who has limited time. Mail order firms particularly, are aimed at those customers who prefer to shop, as it were, from home.

The growth of hypermarkets and edge of city shopping centres

These can provide self-service, a bigger range of goods and greater volume of stock at reduced prices (this results from their rapid turnover allowing them to buy in bulk). Customers can also park their cars at the supermarket, and then complete their shopping under one roof, thereby saving time and money. The growth of superstores in Britain since 1970 is illustrated in Figure 11.11.

A hypermarket differs from a supermarket in that it is usually situated on the edge of urban areas and is aimed at the motorist by trying to attract him or her away from the congested CBD areas.

Figure 11.11 Growth and location of superstores

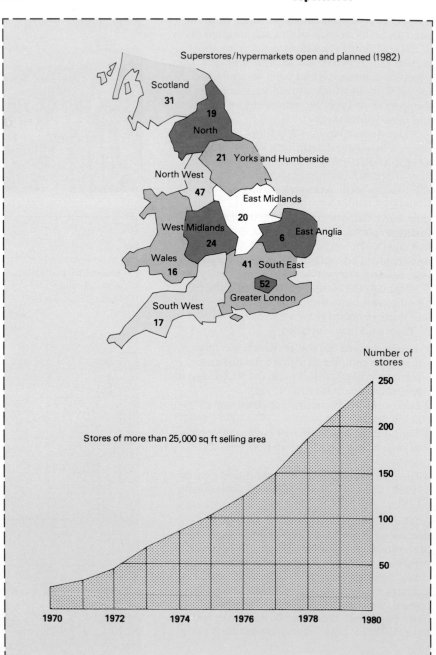

Superstores/hypermarkets open and planned (1982)

Scotland 31
North 19
Yorks and Humberside 21
North West 47
East Midlands 20
West Midlands 24
East Anglia 6
Wales 16
South East 41
Greater London 52
South West 17

Stores of more than 25,000 sq ft selling area

Number of stores

What does a hypermarket provide?

Hypermarkets will have most of the following features:

- A large volume of stock.
- A wide range of goods.
- A warehouse type of layout in a single-storey building.
- Large trolleys for bulk buying.
- Numerous cash checkout points.
- Restaurants, play areas, rest rooms and perhaps even a petrol station.

Where are hypermarkets built?

Some of the main location factors in determining where hypermarkets are built are shown in Figure 11.12.

Where to locate a hypermarket

Figure 11.13 shows three possible sites for a hypermarket. These are labelled A, B and C. If you had to choose an ideal location, would your answer have been similar to one of the following?

A This site would be rejected because it is too far from the large urban areas and is not near enough to a motorway interchange for the delivery of goods and the convenience of shoppers. It would also be refused planning permission by the National Park Planning Board.

Figure 11.12 Factors affecting the location of a hypermarket

B This would also be rejected since land values in this area would be high. There might not, in addition, be sufficient room for such a large building and its car park. This site would also be too far from a motorway access to attract those shoppers who arrive by car.

C This site would be the preferred choice as it has an out-of-town location where land is cheaper and where there is space for any future expansion. It is also next to a motorway interchange, and is easily accessible from the three largest settlements shown on the map.

Figure 11.13 Possible sites for a hypermarket

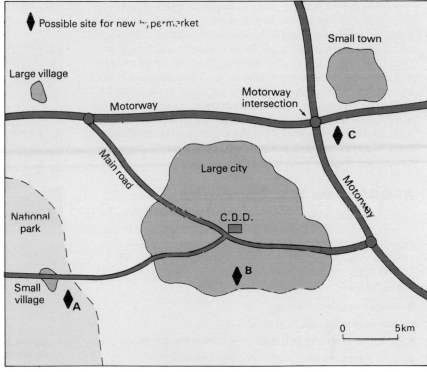

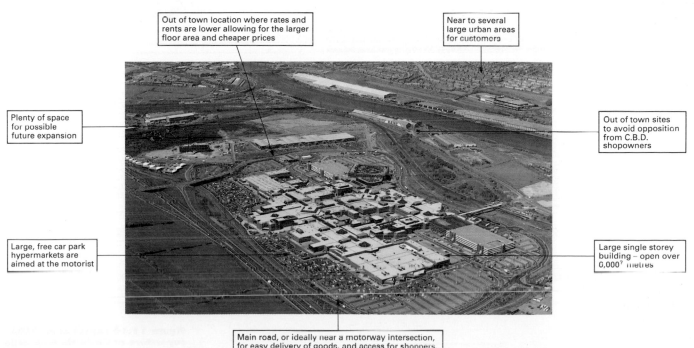

Out of town location where rates and rents are lower allowing for the larger floor area and cheaper prices

Near to several large urban areas for customers

Plenty of space for possible future expansion

Out of town sites to avoid opposition from C.B.D. shopowners

Large, free car park hypermarkets are aimed at the motorist

Large single storey building – open over 0,000² metres

Main road, or ideally near a motorway intersection, for easy delivery of goods, and access for shoppers. No traffic congestion as in C.B.D.

● SUPERSTORES

The ASDA environment

ASDA were the superstore pioneers of the late 1960s and remain the undisputed leaders in this type of retailing in Britain. They have built up a reputation with bright, well-designed, efficient superstores based on customer requirements. The original principle of quality products at competitive prices has been matched to that of shopping convenience with extra-wide aisles, clearly marked departments and fast check-outs. Modern improvements in the internal design of stores, first trialled at Leamington Spa in 1985, have led to the 'three zone layout' based on Clothing and Footwear, Household goods and Grocery and Fresh Foods. The Household and Leisure business, which includes records and small electrical items, ceramics, glass and linens, has been a recent innovation (Figure 11.16). Large car parks for up to 1500 vehicles and free bus services at most stores have helped to bring the ASDA shopping environment within the reach of most British households (3.7 million people shop at ASDA every week) as well as having changed the nation's shopping habits over the last quarter of a century.

ASDA's own label marketing

ASDA introduced its own brand products in 1986 aiming to either match other leading brands in quality, but at a lower price, or to offer high quality products unique to ASDA. By 1990, over 8000 such 'own label' products, out of a total of 40 000 different items, were on sale. The present concept of ASDA Brand is to:

- improve customer choice,
- introduce new, original products,
- give the company better control over what it sells,
- strengthen the company's identity and image.

Tomorrow's technology today

Most stores have computerised check-out systems. Most products have, on their labels, a series of black lines and numbers. This is a bar code. The arrangement of lines on the bar code differs for every product. A bar code is a coded message which tells the computer which product has been selected and how much it costs. As the product is passed through the checkout, a scanner reads the bar code using a light beam and the details of the purchased product are printed onto the till receipt.

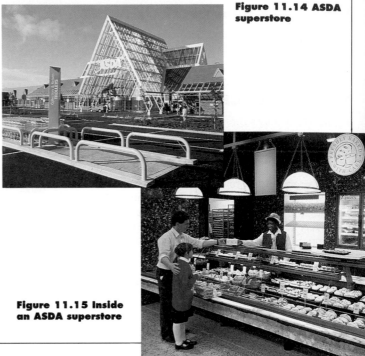

Figure 11.14 ASDA superstore

Figure 11.15 Inside an ASDA superstore

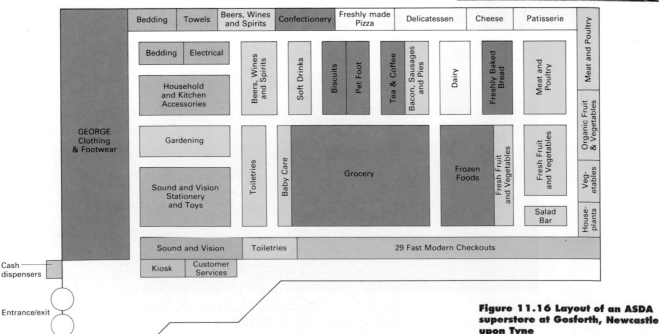

Figure 11.16 Layout of an ASDA superstore at Gosforth, Newcastle upon Tyne

The location of ASDA stores

ASDA began trading in 1965. By 1981 it had 65 superstores and 16 smaller units employing 20 000 people. Following the acquisition of 60 Gateway stores in June 1990, ASDA operated 200 stores employing 68 000 people. New stores are continually being built (by 1992, 75 000 people will be employed in 230 stores) and existing ones modernised.

Since ASDA's parent company, Associated Dairies, was based in Leeds, many of the earlier superstores were located in the North of England. Here the ideal sites proved to be edge-of-city locations where land was relatively cheap, there was room for large car parks and future expansion, and with good access to motorways and main roads. By pioneering 'out-of-town' shopping, ASDA helped to relieve congestion in city centres. Although further stores were opened in the North of England during the 1980s, many more were located in the South-east (where, according to ASDA, 'there was a shortage of convenience shopping') and other urban areas in the British Isles (Figure 11.17). At the same time, ASDA set up as a developer and magnet trader, sometimes in an attempt to help revitalise old inner city areas (e.g. Longsight, Manchester) and sometimes to improve local community services (e.g. Estover, Plymouth — Figure 11.18).

ASDA and the environment

While ASDA prides itself on having always been sympathetic to local environments, recently they have increasingly acted upon other 'green' issues. These include:

- Being the first retailer to remove CFCs from all their own-label aerosols.
- Attempting to reduce harmful CFCs in refrigeration and insulating foam.
- Increasing the number of stores with bottle, paper and can banks.
- Selling unleaded petrol at their petrol stations.
- Increasing the range of organically grown fruit and vegetables.
- Own brand household cleaners, washing powders and liquids washing-up liquids, and their own label foam baths, shampoos and soaps, all of which contain 80% biodegradable detergents.

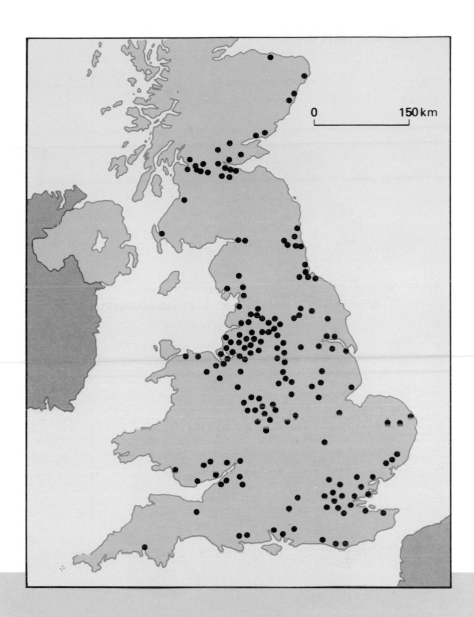

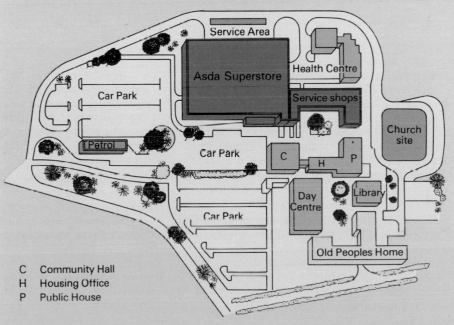

Figure 11.17 ASDA superstore locations in Britain, early 1990s (top)

Figure 11.18 The layout of the Estover district centre, Plymouth (bottom)

C   Community Hall
H   Housing Office
P   Public House

97

○ TRADE AREAS

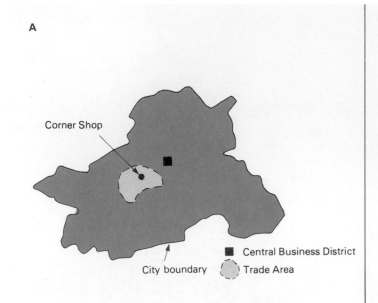

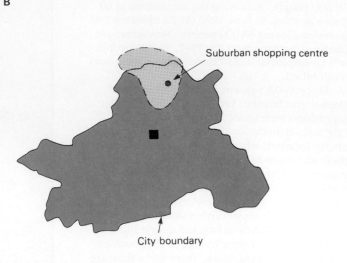

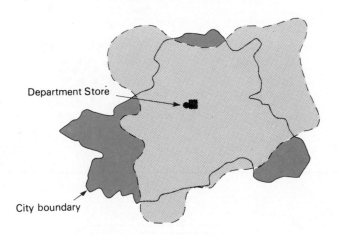

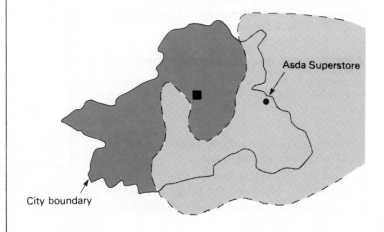

The trade area is the area from which people are prepared to travel in order to shop. The shopkeepers' aim should be to try to attract shoppers from an ever increasing trade area. Different types of shop have different sizes of trade area, and all shops will suffer from competition from rival shops. Figure 11.19 shows the different trade areas of four selected types of shop in Sheffield. Do the following four types also apply to your city?

1 The corner shop in selling mainly convenience goods has a trade area of only a few streets.
2 The suburban shopping parade also sells mainly convenience goods, but although the trade area is larger than the corner shop's by its covering a large housing estate, it still only covers a small geographical area.

3 The department store which sells mainly high-order/comparison goods, attracts its customers from all over the urban area and even beyond.
4 The superstore is likely to attract customers from several urban areas but, as Figure 11.19 shows, fewer people will visit it if they have to cross urban areas.

Large department stores and chain stores will only start a business in a town or city if the trade area contains a sufficiently high number of potential customers (sometimes called the 'sphere of influence') for their large shops to make a profit. The 'threshold population' (the minimum of people in the trade area) is usually 10 000 for a branch of Boots, 60 000 for Sainsbury's, and 50 000 to 100 000 for a Marks & Spencer or a John Lewis branch.

Figure 11.19 Trade areas — Sheffield

Look at Figure 11.20 and answer the questions which follow:

1 If you lived in Town A how often, and for what reasons, would you shop in City X and City Y?

2 If you lived in Town B, what sort of goods would you buy locally? Which of the two cities would you usually shop in?

3 If you lived in village M, how often would you shop in the village, in Town B, and in City X?

4 If you were a shopkeeper in City X, what would you do to attract customers from Town B (who might otherwise go to City Y) and from Town D (who previously had never shopped in City X)?

Distributions of shops

Study Figure 11.21 and then describe and give reasons for the distributions of the four types of shops shown. Having gone through the above questions and data you should now complete the table shown as Figure 11.22 which will help to summarise the main points made in this chapter.

Figure 11.20 Competition between trade areas

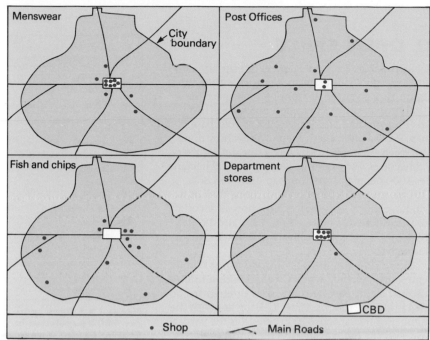

Figure 11.21
Distribution of different types of shops in a city

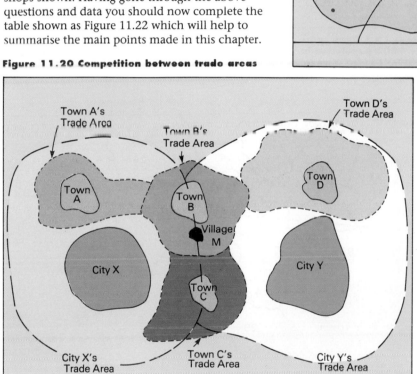

Figure 11.22
Comparison of shopping types

Type of shop	Distance shoppers prepared to travel	Method of travel	Size of trade area	Frequency of visits	Types of goods	Special opening hours	Date when built
Corner shop							
Surburban parade							
C.B.D.							
Hypermarket							

○ OPEN SPACE

All urban areas have open space, but the size and distribution of this open space varies within cities. Figure 12.1 gives the amount of open space per 1000 people in the 33 London boroughs. Using this information, and Figure 12.2 as your base map, draw a choropleth map to show how much land each borough has by using one dot for every 0.5 hectares. For example, Barking has 1.9 hectares per 1000 people, so on the map draw in 3 dots. This means that a borough with many dots in it will have much open space. How do you account for the differences between the 1971 and 1979 figures for **1** outer boroughs, and **2** inner boroughs?

Figure 12.2 also has a line drawn across it and represents a section across Greater London from the west to the east. This line goes through ten of the London boroughs. Draw a histogram with the number of hectares per 1000 people as the vertical axis, and the ten boroughs as the horizontal axis to show how the amount of open space changes across a city. Which areas have the most open space? Which have the least? Westminster is said to be an 'anomaly'. What is an anomaly? Why should Westminster be one on this graph?

Figure 12.3 shows the beginnings of a scattergraph. This scattergraph provides a correlation between two variables. Do you think that this correlation proves that the amount of open space increases with distance from the city centre? Figures 12.1 and 12.2 show that Barking has 1.9 hectares per 1000 people and the nearest point of its boundary is 10 km from the centre of the City.

This information (as well as the information on Barnet) has been plotted on Figure 12.3. Complete this scattergraph for all the London boroughs. Now draw in a best fit line to pass near to all the points on the graph. If this line slopes upwards to the right (Figure 12.4) it is a positive correlation. This means that open space does increase with distance from the city. If the line slopes downwards to the right (Figure 12.4) it is a negative correlation, meaning that as distance from the city centre increases the amount of open space decreases. (This is obviously not true in this example.)

Borough		Hectares		Borough		Hectares	
		1971	1979			1971	1979
1	Barking	1.7	1.9	18	Hounslow	2.7	2.0
2	Barnet	2.3	2.8	19	Islington	0.2	0.3
3	Bexley	2.7	3.1	20	Kensington and Chelsea	0.3	0.3
4	Brent	1.4	1.5	21	Kingston upon Thames	1.8	1.7
5	Bromley	2.8	3.4	22	Lambeth	0.7	0.8
6	Camden	1.6	1.8	23	Lewisham	1.1	1.8
7	City of London	0.0	0.0	24	Merton	2.1	4.3
8	Croydon	3.7	3.7	25	Newham	0.6	0.8
9	Ealing	2.3	1.8	26	Redbridge	1.8	3.3
10	Enfield	2.5	2.9	27	Richmond upon Thames	11.5	21.1
11	Greenwich	2.6	3.0	28	Southwark	0.6	0.8
12	Hackney	1.2	1.5	29	Sutton	2.4	2.5
13	Hammersmith	0.8	0.9	30	Tower Hamlets	0.7	0.9
14	Haringey	1.9	1.7	31	Waltham Forest	1.0	2.6
15	Harrow	1.9	2.1	32	Wandsworth	1.3	2.1
16	Havering	2.1	2.9	33	City of Westminster	1.9	2.1
17	Hillingdon	5.3	4.9				

Figure 12.1 Open space per 1000 population in Greater London boroughs

Figure 12.2 Greater London boroughs

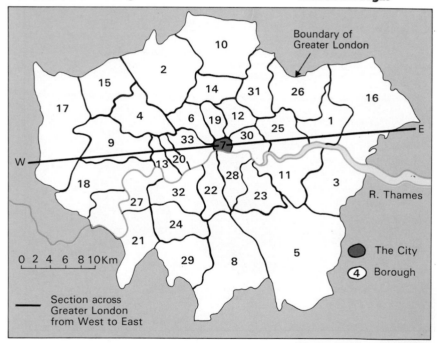

Figure 12.4 Positive and negative correlation

Figure 12.3 Open space and distance from city centre

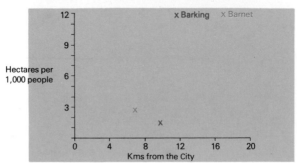

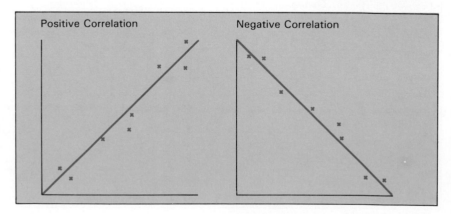

Distribution of open space in Leeds

Figure 12.5 shows the types and distribution of open space in a large city, in this case, Leeds. Public open space is defined as land which is free for everyone's use.

Notice that:

■ Little open space exists near the CBD where land values are high and where the city was built in pre-planning days.

■ Small parks begin some 2 km from the CBD where land values begin to decrease.

■ Recreation grounds are widely spread out to cater for individual housing estates, and are numerous due to the size of Leeds.

■ More parks lie to the North-east which is less industrialised and has better quality housing.

■ The large parks, including lakes and golf courses, are found near the city boundary where land is both available and cheaper.

■ There is a limited amount of woodland, but patches are found nearer the boundary where they have been left as a result of development plans.

Country parks — recreation near to urban areas

Due to pressures from the growing number of visitors on the countryside, coast and National Parks in Britain, the Government believed that if the needs of townspeople for countryside recreation were to be met, and the countryside was not to be spoiled, then the range of choice available to townspeople should be enlarged. It was thought that country parks should make it easier for town dwellers to enjoy their leisure in the open without travelling too far and without adding to the congestion on the roads. At the same time they ought to ease the pressure on the more remote and solitary places (Figure 12.6).

A country park is not a wild, remote area on the scale of the National Park, nor is it a municipal recreation or sports ground. Many country parks provide the family with small, secluded areas of woods or open parkland where they can study natural history or simply absorb the peaceful beauty of the countryside. Others are much larger with places to bathe, fish, sail, ride and enjoy many other informal recreational activities. There are car parking and toilet facilities in all of them. Some also have refreshment facilities, picnic sites, information centres and wardens to help you to enjoy your visit.

Figure 12.7 summarises some of the differences between a local neighbourhood park and an edge of city or country park.

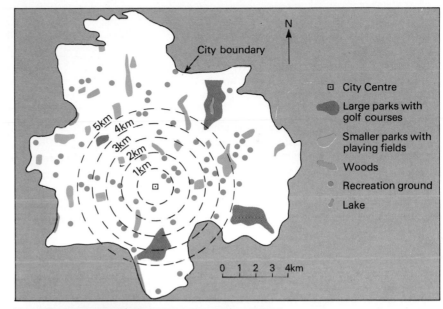

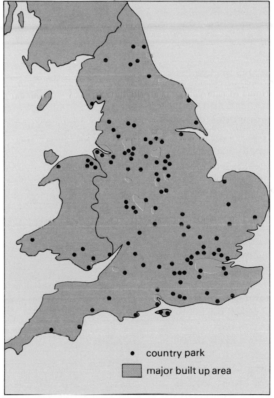

Figure 12.5 Distribution of open space in Leeds

Figure 12.6 Location of Country Parks

Figure 12.7 Differences between urban and rural parks

	Local/neighbourhood park	Large edge of city/Regional/Country Park
Size	A few hectares	Usually over 25 hectares
Distance travelled	Less than 1 km	Up to 50 km
Transport used	Foot	Car, bus
When visited in the week	Evenings. Afternoons in holidays	Weekends
When visited in the year	All year	Summer mainly
Length of visit	1 to 2 hours	Half to a full day
Main users	Mothers and small children in p.m. Children in evening	Families
Amenities	Swings and roundabouts	Lakes, team games, nature trails
Summary	Accessibility is more important than size or amenities	Amenities are more important than time — distance — cost in getting there

○ AMENITIES

Figure 12.8 shows the distribution and location of leisure amenities in a typical British city. Unlike the distribution of open space in a city, the closer one lives to the city centre, the greater are the number of indoor amenities available. This is partly due to:

- Higher land values in the city centre which means that higher admission charges have to be made.
- The nearer to the centre, the greater is the degree of accessibility for all the inhabitants.
- Those amenities found within 1 km of the centre are usually located along main roads for the purposes of accessibility and lower rates.
- The two amenities, which are sited 5 km from the centre, are in large modern housing estates.

Professional football grounds are usually located in inner city areas (Figures 12.8 and 12.9) for the following reasons:

- The clubs were founded at a time when inner city areas were being developed.
- Accessibility along main roads.
- Car parking facilities are available in cleared housing districts.
- The grounds are usually near to bus and rail stations which can serve the supporters of rival teams.
- Inner city areas have traditionally had high local population densities.

One leisure amenity not given in Figure 12.8 is an ice-rink. The local council in this typical example decided to build one realising the importance of accessibility for attracting as many users as possible. The various districts in this imaginary town are shown in Figure 12.9. If you were a planner where would you place the ice-rink?

In order to arrive at this decision you will need to complete the table (Figure 12.10) in the following way. For every district you pass through, count one point as being a likely delay. So, for example, to get from Gosforth to Benton, you have to pass through Salford and so a score of two is given. The district with the lowest score is the most accessible. When you have completed the table answer these questions:

1 Which point is most accessible? Why would an ice-rink not be built here?
2 Which is the next best area?
3 Which is the poorest area for the ice-rink? Why is this?

Leisure amenity	In CBD	Within 1km from CBD	2km from CBD	3km from CBD	4km from CBD	5km from CBD
Professional football ground	0	1	0	0	0	0
Swimming Pool	0	1	0	0	0	0
Theatre	2	0	0	0	0	0
Cinema	3	1	0	0	0	0
Sports centre	0	2	0	0	0	1
Bingo hall	6	4	2	0	0	1

Figure 12.8 Distribution of leisure amenities in a large city

Figure 12.9 Possible location for an ice rink in a large city

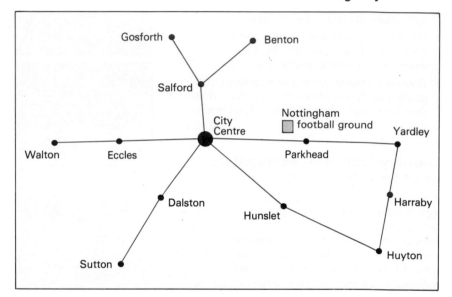

	Gosforth	Salford	Benton	City Centre	Walton	Eccles	Sutton	Dalston	Hunslet	Parkhead	Yardley	Harraby	Huyton	
Gosforth	-	1	2	2	4	3	4	3	3	3	4	5	4	38
Salford	1	-	1	1	3	2	3	2	2	2	3	4	3	27
Benton	2	1	-											
City Centre	2	1		-										
Walton	4	3			-									
Eccles	3	2				-								
Sutton	4	3					-							
Dalston	3	2						-						
Hunslet	3	2							-					
Parkhead	3	2								-				
Yardley	4	3									-			
Harraby	5	4										-		
Huyton	.4	3											-	

Figure 12.10 Matrix for Figure 12.9

The Concordia Leisure Centre, Cramlington New Town

The location of the Concordia

Concordia is situated in the centre of Cramlington New Town next to the undercover shopping area, the library, and car parks (Figure 8.29). It was located here because:

- Ease of accessibility from all over Cramlington and the surrounding area.
- Land was available for the development of the centre, and the associated car parks.
- The centrality of the site would encourage the many users needed to pay for the high rates.
- Being a new town, the provision of leisure amenities was a key factor in the planning scheme.

Size and nature of area served by Concordia

Most members come from new town itself, i.e. within a radius of 2 km. Efforts were made, in the planning of the centre, to cater for all members of the community. Although the numbers of visitors decrease after 2 km, this decrease is less rapid if visitors live along main roads into Cramlington, or in adjacent settlements which either lack their own leisure centres, or have one with fewer amenities.

To attract members, the centre is open seven days a week, from 0910 hours to 2300 hours, and throughout the whole year.

Questions

1 Planners have to take into consideration all members of the community. Using Figure 12.11:
 a Say how, if at all, the following groups of people are catered for: teenagers; young married couples with small children; middle-aged; elderly; disabled.
 b Say which activities can be grouped as
 i) active, ii) passive.

2 Using Figure 12.12, describe and give reasons for the seasonal variation in the numbers using the Leisure Centre.

3 How could a leisure centre, such as Concordia, attempt to attract even more members?

4 How does the location of Concordia within Cramlington New Town (Figure 8.29) differ from the location of a similar leisure centre in an older British town?

Figure 12.11 Concordia Leisure Centre, Cramlington New Town, Northumberland

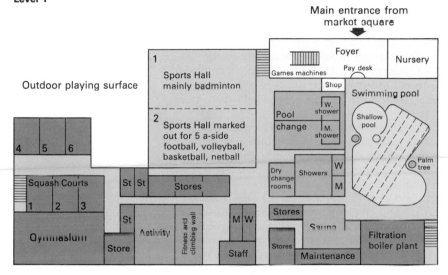

Level 1

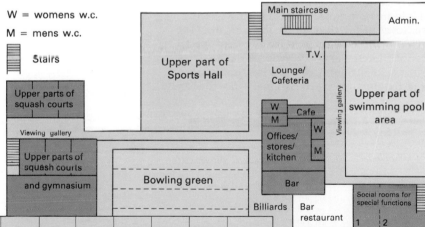

Level 2

Figure 12.12 Seasonal use of amenities in Concordia Leisure Centre

Activity	April 4 wks	May 5 wks	June 4 wks	July 4 wks	Aug 5 wks	Sept 4 wks	Oct 4 wks	Nov 5 wks	Dec 4 wks	Jan 5 wks	Feb 4 wks	March 4 wks	Average
% of time that activity was used													
Squash	78	74	69	73	69	76	80	80	73	78	87	84	77
Main Hall	77	65	65	68	66	65	74	74	68	71	86	86	72
Bowls	61	16	7	8	12	42	78	74	69	76	77	82	50
Swimming (% users out of max.)	36	38	31	39	61	33	33	26	24	35	49	44	37

○ HOLIDAYS

Tourism is a major British industry. It is concerned with providing services for people who wish to spend some time away from home, usually on holiday. The accepted definition of a holiday is the spending of four or more nights away from home. Figure 12.13 shows, with examples, some of the historical factors as well as those operative today, which have led to the location and growth of British tourist resorts and the development of tourist areas.

The location of tourist resorts

Long-stay resorts in Britain are usually on the coast (Figure 12.14), have sandy beaches, and are in areas which have high sunshine and limited rain. These resorts are also accessible by road and/or rail from urban areas.

Day-trip resorts are also located on the coast, having good communications with nearby urban areas. Cultural and historic resorts tend to be inland and are usually situated in capital cities or in cities having castles and cathedrals. The highland areas of Scotland, on the other hand, have a snow cover for several months. This makes them suitable for winter sports, and resorts have grown up in these areas. The two most popular types of holiday are sun, sea and sand holidays Figure 12.15 and mountains and water (Figures 12.16 and 12.17).

Many parts of Britain which have attractive scenery, historic sites and important habitats for wildlife are now protected areas (Figure 12.18). The Government, through the department of the Environment, protects some 5000 Sites of Special Scientific Interest and 279 National Nature Reserves. In England and Wales landscapes are protected through the 10 National Parks, the New Forest and the Norfolk Broads, 16 Areas of Outstanding Natural Beauty and 39 Sections of Heritage Coast. In Scotland 40 Natural Scenic Areas cover 13% of the land area while 80% of the coastline is a protected zone. Other interested organisations include the RSPB, the National Trust, the Woodland Trust, the Countryside Commission and the World Wildlife Organisation.

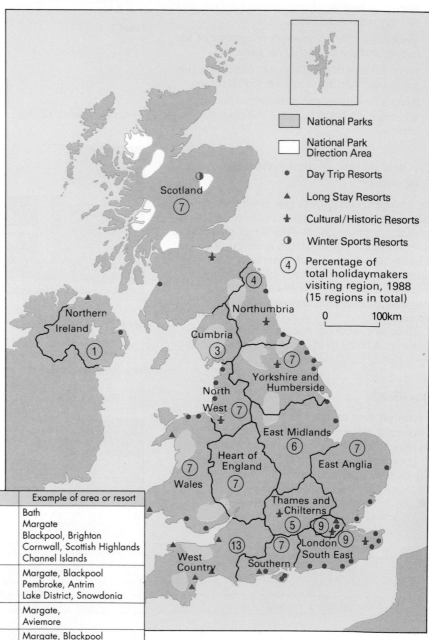

Figure 12.14 Location of major holiday resorts

National Parks

National Park Direction Area

● Day Trip Resorts

▲ Long Stay Resorts

✚ Cultural/Historic Resorts

◖ Winter Sports Resorts

④ Percentage of total holidaymakers visiting region, 1988 (15 regions in total)

0   100km

Scotland ⑦

Northumbria

Northern Ireland ①

Cumbria ③

④

⑦ Yorkshire and Humberside

North West ⑦

East Midlands ⑥

Heart of England ⑦

Wales ⑦

East Anglia ⑦

Thames and Chilterns ⑤

London South East ⑨

⑨

West Country ⑬

Southern ⑦

Figure 12.13 Factors affecting the location of the holiday industry

Factors	Specific examples	Example of area or resort
1. Transport and accessibilty	i) Early resorts. (Stage-Coach) Spa towns ii) Water transport (18th century) iii) Railways iv) Car and Coach v) Plane	Bath Margate Blackpool, Brighton Cornwall, Scottish Highlands Channel Islands
2. Scenery	i) Sandy coasts of outstanding beauty ii) Coasts of outstanding beauty iii) Mountains, lakes and rivers	Margate, Blackpool Pembroke, Antrim Lake District, Snowdonia
3. Weather	i) Hot, dry, sunny summers ii) Snow	Margate, Aviemore
4. Accommodation	i) Hotels and boarding house resorts ii) Holiday camps iii) Caravan parks and camp sites	Margate, Blackpool Minehead, Pwllheli National and forest parks
5. Amenities	i) Culture and historic (castles, cathedrals, birthplaces ii) Active amenities (sailing, golf, water-skiing) iii) Passive amenities (shop, cinemas)	York, Edinburgh Kielder, St. Andrews Most resorts
6. Greater affluence More leisure time Earlier retirement Shorter working week	i) Increased demand for new types of leisure (e.g. pony trekking, hang-gliding) ii) Over-use of existing amenities	North Yorks. Moors Parts of national parks
7. Advertising		Torbay

Figure 12.15 The beach at Weymouth, Dorset

Figure 12.16 Crummock Water, Cumbria

Figure 12.17 The Mourne Mountains, County Down, Northern Ireland

Figure 12.18 Nature and landscape conservation

National Parks (England and Wales)

Areas of Outstanding Natural Beauty (England, Wales and N. Ireland)

National Scenic Areas (Scotland)

Heritage Coasts (England and Wales)

Other special protected areas

Long Distance Routes

O CHANGING PATTERNS

The kinds of holidays people now take and where they take them have undergone a number of noticeable changes:

- **Frequency of holidays** In 1977, 59% of British people had a long holiday (that is, a holiday lasting four or more nights). By 1988 there was an increasing number taking more than one holiday per year (Figure 12.19a).

- **Short-stay holidays** (mini-breaks) where people were away from home for three evenings or less increased.

- **Location of holiday**. In the early part of this century most holidays were taken at the seaside with the traditional British coastal resort being linked by rail to the nearby large city. Since the 1960s many people wanting a 'sun, sand and sea' holiday have gone abroad. In 1988 over 53% of people staying in Britain visited urban centres (Figure 12.19b) and only 24% the seaside.

- **Change in holiday transport** More holidaymakers now use their own car for greater convenience and mobility, consequently fewer people are making use of public transport (Figure 12.19c).

- **Accommodation** There has been a sharp decline in the use of the more traditional 'boarding house' and hotel and a corresponding increase in self-catering holidays such as camping, caravaning and rented flats (Figure 12.19d). The most recent trend is the growth in the number of people who stay with friends and relatives.

- **Money spent on holidays** has also increased (Figure 12.19e) — in 1987 the average British family spent £258.

- **People are tending to travel further,** and to take more unusual and exotic holidays. More people are taking either their main holiday abroad, or have a week and a series of weekend breaks in Britain.

- **Britain's balance of tourists has also changed.** Even in the mid-1980s Britain received more money from visitors from overseas than was spent by the British themselves going abroad. This helped our balance of payments. The period 1986-1988 saw a reversal in this movement (Figure 12.19e, f and g) although the high mortgage rates and airport delays are credited for the increase in British people holidaying 'at home' in 1989.

The problems which face tourism

- **Overcrowding** at certain times of the year causes various difficulties during the summer period, such as trying to find a space to park, or room in a cafe, or a hotel.

- **Greater congestion** resulting from increased car ownership, especially on those major roads

leading to resorts or places devoted to summer activities. Congestion also occurs at weekends when most people either begin or end their holiday, or go out for day trips (Figure 12.20).

- **Conflicts** arise between recreation interests competing for limited space. For example, water skiing may compete with swimming and fishing on lakes; similarly downhill skiing may conflict with cross-country skiing.

- **Seasonal unemployment** comes to coastal resorts in the winter since there is no need for deck chair and car park attendants, nor extra staff in hotels or in souvenir shops. (Figure 12.21.)

a Holidays in a year (%)

	1977	1983	1988
More than two	6	7	8
Two holidays	13	16	24
One holiday	40	40	36
No holiday	41	37	32

b Location of holidays in Britain

	1987	1988
Seaside	31	24
Countryside	27	19
Small town	17	24
Large town or city	14	18
London	8	11
Others	3	4

c Main transport to destination (%)

	1951	1983	1988
Car	27	69	74
Bus (and coach tours)	27	11	7
Train	46	12	12
Air	0	8	7

d Types of accommodation used in Britain (%)

	1961	1983	1988
Hotels	46	21	17
Bed and Breakfast	6	6	5
Camp, caravan, rented	17	23	20
Friends	21	46	51
Holiday camps	9	2	3
Second homes	1	2	1
Others (e.g. boat)	0	0	3

e Money spent on holidays by UK residents (£ million)

	1977	1983	1988
In Britain	1800	5350	7850
Overseas	975	4425	8525
Total	2775	9775	16 375

f Balance of money spent by visitors (£ million)

	1985	1988
By UK residents overseas	4460	7150
By visitors to the UK	6110	5400

g Balance of visitors (millions)

	1988
UK residents going overseas	27.4
Overseas visitors to UK	17.3

(Source - British Tourist Authority).

Figure 12.19 Changing holiday patterns

Figure 12.20 Seasonal pressures on transport - ferry queues in the summer

- Attempts have been made by hotel owners to increase the number of guests, and to lengthen the tourist season by means of cheaper out-of-season rates, catering for educational visits, keeping costs at a minimum and increasing the service, and opening at lunch time for bar snacks for all the family, thereby aiming at the day-tripper.

  What attempts, do you think, have tourist resorts made to overcome the seasonal nature of holidays? Can you add to a list which includes Blackpool's illuminations and Tower Circus, Brighton's Party Conferences, and the hoteliers in the Lake District who offer one free night for every three nights booked?

- An increase in the number of elderly and retired people with more spare time as well as the 'early retirement' workers.

- The impact of the recession resulting in more favourable exchange rates has meant that holidays abroad are relatively cheaper than at home — a trend reversed in 1989.

- The growing demand for a wider range of activities (e.g. hang-gliding and wind-surfing) also demands more space and facilities.

- The second homes used, especially in rural Wales, by urban dwellers for only a few days in a year which, in turn, deprives locals of housing accommodation.

- The increase in pollution from noise, litter and vandalism.

- Uncertainties of the British climate mean winter skiers prefer the Alps, and summer sunbathers the Mediterranean.

**Figure 12.21 The seasonal nature of
a) tourism
b) business conferences, 1988**

The impact of tourism on local communities

The impact of tourism has both advantages and disadvantages for the inhabitants and the environment.

Advantages

- Increased trade for shopkeepers.
- Jobs for local inhabitants.
- Improved communication links.
- New forms of entertainment created especially for teenagers.
- Increase in money arising from rates from new hotels and leisure amenities.

Disadvantages

- Noise and congestion affect the elderly and retired.
- Jobs are often only seasonal.
- Road and car park congestion.
- The visual appearance of a town can be spoilt by new buildings and litter.
- Higher land prices means land, including agricultural land, may be sold for development.
- Higher costs may force locals out.
- Small guest houses lose trade to modern hotels, holiday camps and caravan parks.

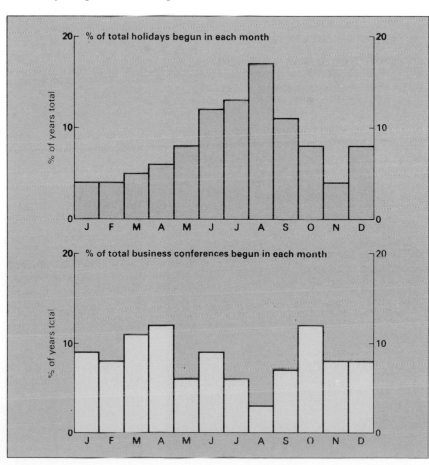

○ IN CITIES

The competition for land in city centres

As has been shown in earlier chapters, the centre of a town or city is known as the Central Business District. Figure 13.1 is an aerial picture of the City of London. By referring to this, you should be able to list several uses or functions of this central area. The importance of this CBD is due to its having the greatest accessibility within the city. This is because most of the main roads from the suburbs and surrounding towns meet here.

Because many people gather in this zone, businesses, and especially specialist shops and offices, will compete for key sites (Figure 13.2). This competition will push up land values so that it is only the big businesses that will be able to afford to pay the resulting high rates and rents.

Figure 13.3 is an isopleth map showing that the highest land values are in the CBD. If you study this map together with Figure 13.4 (which is a land value cross section of the city) you will notice that:

- Land values are highest in the CBD.
- Land values decrease rapidly towards the city boundary.
- Land values tend to remain high along main roads.
- Land values also form smaller peaks away from the CBD where major roads meet.

Also in the CBD, but not in the actual core, are other competitors for the most accessible parts but because they are less profitable or non-profit making (e.g. museum, library, football ground), they have to be located instead around the central core where land values decrease. Figure 13.2 shows the 'functional zones' where all the competitors for land are concerned, for example, either with education or with entertainment.

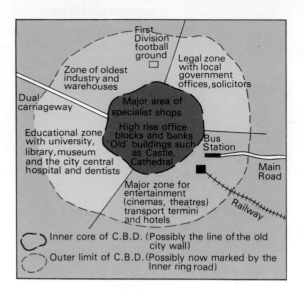

Figure 13.2 Land use and functional zones in the Central Business District (CBD)

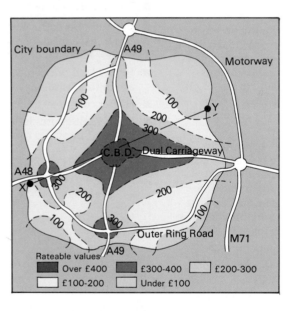

Figure 13.3 Land values in a typical city

Figure 13.1 Competition for land - City of London

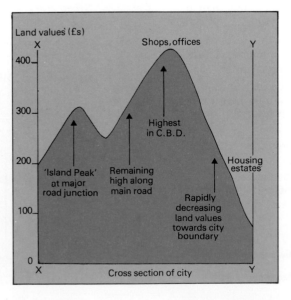

Figure 13.4 Land values across a city

The competition for land at the urban-rural fringe

During the inter-war period, London expanded outwards into the surrounding countryside at a rapid rate. The fastest growth took place near to main roads and the recently extended Underground lines. In an attempt to prevent future growth of this kind the Green Belt Policy was introduced in 1947. A Green Belt is an area of land around a town or city where the erection of houses and other buildings is severely restricted and the open character of the country is preserved. Its purpose is to strictly control any further outward growth of urban areas, and to preserve areas of countryside for farming and for the recreational needs of that urban area. This belt extended all around the city. However, within the built-up area itself, two types of Inner Green Areas were to be left untouched. These were the central parks (such as Hyde Park) and the commons (such as Wimbledon and Hampstead Heath).

However, this and Green Belts around other British cities soon came under pressure from various developers. Nowadays the Government is still under constant pressure to give permission for development. Figure 13.5 depicts some of the likely competitors for land in the so-called urban-rural fringe which surrounds cities whether or not they have a Green Belt.

These pressures have led local authorities to rethink their policies on Green Belts. Some planners believe that a system of green wedges would be more practical than a complete circle of green. These wedges would keep green areas close to the city centre, and yet enable growth in certain controlled directions.

Figure 13.5 Competition for land in the rural-urban fringe

Green Belts since 1985

Four changes are affecting future land use in Green Belts.

1 A decline in pressure from quarrying, as reserves are exhausted, and farming, as land is 'set aside' and taken out of production (page 19).

2 Increased pressure from the environmental lobby seeking to protect and conserve the landscape and its wildlife.

3 The abolition of the Metropolitan County Boroughs e.g. Greater London and Greater Manchester, who had controlled planning decisions in their local Green Belts. However it has been acknowledged that while these authorities had been successful in preventing building they had not always seen that land was used to its maximum potential.

4 The winding down of the post-war New Town Corporations. In 1985 Consortium Developments Ltd applied to build, at Tillingham Hall in Essex, the first of 15 proposed 'new country towns, around London. Each new settlement was to have about 5000 homes ranging from those for first time buyers to those for high salary earners, would house 12 000 to 15 000 people and cover 300 to 400 hectares. Each would have its own schools, shops and medical centres as well as other service and leisure amenities. The aim was also to create up to 2000 jobs in light and hi-tech industries (page 54). The opening of the M25, built on Green Belt land, has created extra pressure on the environment. Motorway interchanges are prime sites for large retail outlets, hypermarkets (page 95), hotels, office development and science parks (page 55) while the extra traffic has increased various forms of pollution.

The 1990s will see changes in the limits and use of Green Belts.

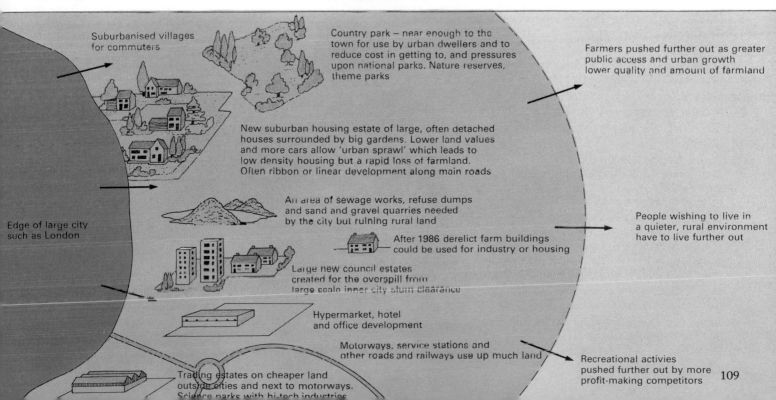

◌ THE COUNTRYSIDE

The role of National Park planning boards

The aim of the planning boards is to look after the organisation and provision of services and amenities and the use of land for the purposes of conserving the landscape and providing recreation. These boards were also established to look after areas for the purpose of the preservation of natural scenery and wild life, largely in the interests of public enjoyment.

At the present rate of consumption, an area equivalent in size to Leicestershire is swallowed up by development (e.g. buildings, gardens, roads, etc.) every ten years. And every year, more people want to get away every weekend from the towns and cities where most of them live and work. Every year there is less countryside for them to get away to.

Although National Parks have been protected from excessive small scale commercial and residential development, large scale quarrying and reservoirs have been allowed to intrude on an incongruous scale in some parks because of decisions taken at national level. It is the role of the National Park planning boards to ensure that the quality of the countryside is not sacrificed for short-term economic gain. (Figure 13.6).

The threats to Britain's National Parks

Some of the factors which are likely to endanger the preservation of the National Parks in Britain are:

- More roads and faster roads with increasing accessibility (Figure 10.12). Twenty-five million people live within a three-hour drive of the Lake District National Park (Figure 13.7). What do you think would happen if they all visited it on the same day?

- The increasing number of cars means more car parks, toilets and other amenities.

- More reservoirs, such as Snowdonia's two pumped water schemes, are taking up valuable land.

- Increase in forestry.

- Farmers are enclosing more land as, for example, on Exmoor where government improvement grants have led to one-seventh of the area being ploughed up and fenced off.

- Mining and quarrying corporations who, although providing jobs for the local people and valuable minerals for the country, leave more scars in the landscape and can create 500 tonnes of waste for each ton of mineral mined.

- More industries are being set up in areas of high unemployment.

- Army training grounds still exist on Dartmoor, and low flying jets constantly create noise over the parks.

Problems	Attempted solutions
Footpaths worn away	New routes planned; signposted routes; artificial surfaces laid
Destruction of vegetation	Areas fenced off; education of visitors
Litter, vandalism, trespass	Provision of picnic areas with litter bins; park wardens
Cars parked on grass verges or in narrow lanes	Car parks; one-way systems; park and ride schemes
Congestion on narrow roads	Roads closed to traffic in tourist season/week ends; park and ride; encouraged to use minibuses, cycles or to walk
Heavy lorries, local traffic and tourist traffic	Scenic routes separating local and tourist traffic
'Honeypots' (views, cafes)	Develop alternative honeypots, direct visitors to other attractions
Conflict of users, e.g. **a** local farmers/tourists **b** between tourists	Restricting tourist access to footpaths and bridlepaths. Separating activities e.g. water skiing and angling
New cafés, car parks, and caravan parks.	Screened behind trees. Only certain natural colours allowed in paint schemes.

- Hikers and climbers wear away footpaths.

- The purchase of second homes by the more wealthy urban dweller at the same time deprives locals of houses and creates 'ghost' villages for much of the year.

- More caravan and camping sites are springing up to serve the seasonal self-catering tourist.

- More visitors are creating noise and threatening wild life — both plants and animals.

- Archaeological sites and historic buildings are being destroyed by vandalism.

- Traditional village life, its own particular visual character and the type of services provided are changing.

- There is a lack of money to maintain the parks. More money has been spent in one year on the 'Concorde' airplane than on all our National Parks since their creation.

Figure 13.6 How planning in a National Park can help to solve problems such as over-use, congestion and conflicts of use

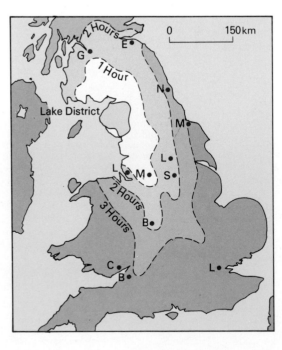

Figure 13.7 Travelling time to the Lake District National Park

Conflicts which are caused by competition for land

Whether it is a new road proposal, a new quarry to be opened up, a new reservoir to be built, a new caravan camp to be created or an increase in forestry, there are always several groups of people in favour of the proposal and several groups against. It is the role of National Park planning boards to consider all conflicting views before making their recommendations and decisions.

Planning a dual carriageway through a National Park

Below are some possible views of groups of people favouring and opposing the proposal to build a dual carriageway through the middle of a National Park, and to by-pass a small town in that area. After reading through these views, decide what you would do if you were a National Park planner, then draw up similar views for and against:

1 The building of a new reservoir.
2 The development of a new quarry.

Honeypots

The National Parks include many of the nation's 'honeypots' — areas of attractive scenery (Malham Cove in the Yorkshire Dales), or of historic interest (the Roman Wall in the Northumberland Park) to which tourists swarm in large numbers. The problem is how can the honeypots' natural beauty, their unspoilt quality (the essence of their appeal) to be preserved while providing facilities for the hordes who arrive at peak summer periods? At Malham Cove steps have been cut into the limestone to safeguard paths. It is estimated that £ 1½million is needed to repair the six paths leading to the top of Snowdon where, on a summer's day, 2500 people might reach the summit. Parts of the 400 km Pennine Way have had to have artifical surfaces laid as in places the tracks of walkers have penetrated over a metre into the peat. The footpaths on the Roman Wall are being eroded and, as soil is washed away, the foundations of the wall are being exposed.

Figure 13.8 Quarrying in the Peak District National Park

For

The Tourist With a dual carriageway the tourist could reach the National Park more quickly, and travel to parks further afield. The tourist could also avoid congestion in the small town, slow moving heavy lorries and tractors, and could see more of the park in a short time without leaving the car.

The heavy lorry driver working at the quarry. Wider roads, gentler gradients, and slow lanes would be created with the construction of a dual carriageway, and perhaps also a special road which would separate heavy lorries from tourist traffic.

The industrial firm beyond the National Park. This firm would be able to get its raw materials faster, and move its manufactured goods out more quickly. It might also save money by reduced transport times. New customers would be attracted and a bigger market created. This might lead as well to the growth of a subsidiary industry as executives would be attracted by the environment of the park.

A retired couple living in small town. The by-pass would mean less noise, fewer traffic fumes, and less danger, due to a decrease in traffic.

The farmer's wife There would be more potential Bed and Breakfast guests; surplus farm produce could also be sold.

The local bus company Local services would find it easier to keep to their timetables and tourist parties could be taken further afield.

The young married couple Travelling to work would be made easier.

Against

The shopkeeper in the small town. Loss in trade would result from there being no through traffic. Locals could also travel more quickly to other towns. The shopkeeper would, in addition, find himself paying rates to help build the new road.

The farmer Increased traffic would mean more noise and more air pollution, and a loss of land because wider roads, car parks and picnic areas would be needed. More visitors would trample on his land, knock down walls and bring dogs which might worry the sheep.

The conservationist Conservationists would object to the new road because they believe noise and fumes destroy wild life, roads destroy the visual attractiveness of the area; and footpaths would be eroded. There would also be an increase in litter.

The local cycle club Greater danger would result from faster traffic, more noise and traffic fumes.

The local lorry driver There would be an increase in traffic and lorries might be banned from certain roads.

The young married couple There would be less chance of their being able to buy a home as more commuters could live in the area and house prices would increase.

● MOUNTAINS AND COASTS

Competition for land in the mountains: Aviemore

Before 1964 Aviemore was a small village some 50 kilometres south of Inverness, situated in the narrow valley of the River Spey. The only tourist attractions were trout and salmon fishing, and some long distance walks and rock climbs. To most people it was just a place name along the main A9 road and mainline railway. Then in 1966 the Aviemore Centre was opened. This provided such activities as a theatre, shops, dance hall, indoor swimming pool, sauna, ice-rink, skittle alley, solarium, cinema and artificial ski-slope. The centre was purpose built for tourists interested in active pastimes since the climate favoured those rather than passive pursuits such as sunbathing. Figure 13.9 and the text below show what further development had taken place or was planned by the late 1980s. Which activities do you think can be followed:

1 Throughout the year at Aviemore?
2 In summer?
3 In winter?

In what ways have these pursuits been due to:

1 Climatic conditions?
2 Other physical conditions?
3 Artificially created amenities?

The future for Aviemore

Many problems are now facing Aviemore. Below are some of the factors which will also affect its future:

■ Existing developments in the Cairngorms have capacity for about 5000 skiers and frequently during the weekend, festive season and Easter peaks this limit is reached if not exceeded. The Cairngorm Chairlift Co Ltd applied for outline planning consent to extend their operations westward into Coire an t-Sneachda, Coire an Lochain and Lurchers Gully, adjacent to their frequently overcrowded operations in Coire Cas and Coire na Ciste (corries).

■ The Regional Council eventually refused permission for the Lurcher's Gully development, but, in 1985 approved outline planning permission for a downhill ski development east of Drumochter Pass on the A9 between Blair Atholl and Dalwhinnie.

■ The Cairngorms contain the largest Arctic-Alpine area in the country and naturalists now see this delicate environment being ruined by skiers.

■ Bulldozing to construct the ski-run and new roads leading to the ski-lift areas has increased the erosion of the land.

■ The breeding of such birds as the ptarmigan, golden eagle and osprey, is prevented by the presence of many tourists.

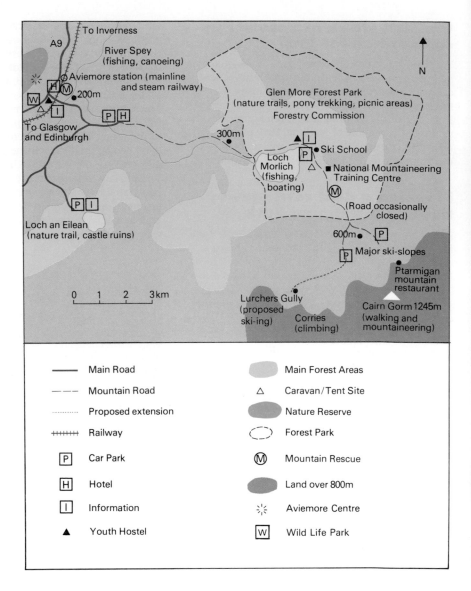

Figure 13.9 Competition for land in the mountains — Aviemore, Cairngorms

■ Tourists may begin forest fires which cause problems for the Forestry Commission.

■ Tourists leave litter; and new roads and buildings spoil the visual appearance for visitors.

■ Canoeists compete with anglers in the River Spey.

■ Cross-country skiers do not want downhill skiers in Lurchers Gully (Figure 13.9).

■ Deer stalkers complain that walkers disturb their quarry.

■ Mountaineers in the high corries do not want skiers nearby.

■ Some groups think that money spent on building the new road could be better used in improving local services.

■ While these new attractions provide new jobs and have reversed the traditional outward migration from this area, they have led to an overuse of parts of the area and its amenities.

■ Property developers come from outside the area and so much of the profit is lost to Aviemore.

Competition for land on the coasts — Blackpool

Blackpool grew rapidly in the last century as its 'Golden Sands' lay within an hour's train ride from the busy industrial towns of Lancashire. Figure 13.10 shows Blackpool as it is today. On the map of the area (Figure 13.11) identify the following places and amenities and try and locate them as they might appear in the photograph.

A Promenade and sea front
B Derby Baths
C North Pier
D The Tower
E Hotels and leisure amenities
F Golf course
G Pleasure Beach
H Railway station
I Central Business District

Competition for land leads to a land use pattern which, although simplified here for Blackpool, is common to most British resorts (Figure 13.11). The large hotels have the best sites along the seafront. They can afford the highest rates, because of their many paying guests wishing to be near, even to overlook, the sea. The boarding houses are found behind the hotels because they can charge visitors less, since they do not have to pay the high rates of the sea front.

The centre of a holiday resort is the Recreational Business District (RBD) which, in Blackpool's case, includes the piers and the Tower. Behind the RBD is the Central Business District, which includes the main shops and banks for both the tourists and the residents. The shops are found either near to the seafront, or on the main roads leading from the transport terminals so that they can attract most trade. The transport terminals (railway and bus stations) are also centrally situated as tourists do not want to walk far to the hotels (annual holidaymakers) or to the beach (day visitors). Further away from the busy seafront are the residential districts using areas of cheaper land values, while even further out are areas of open space.

Coasts attract not just tourists, but permanent residents and industry (Figure 1.16). The result of this may be the eventual destruction of that visual appearance which attracted tourists there in the first place. Tourists may also increase pollution both in the sea and on the beaches (pages 126-127).

Figure 13.10 Blackpool

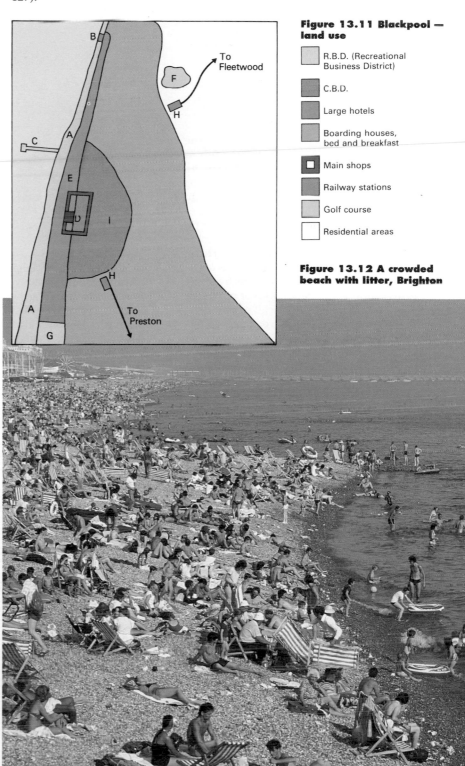

Figure 13.11 Blackpool — land use

- R.B.D. (Recreational Business District)
- C.B.D.
- Large hotels
- Boarding houses, bed and breakfast
- Main shops
- Railway stations
- Golf course
- Residential areas

Figure 13.12 A crowded beach with litter, Brighton

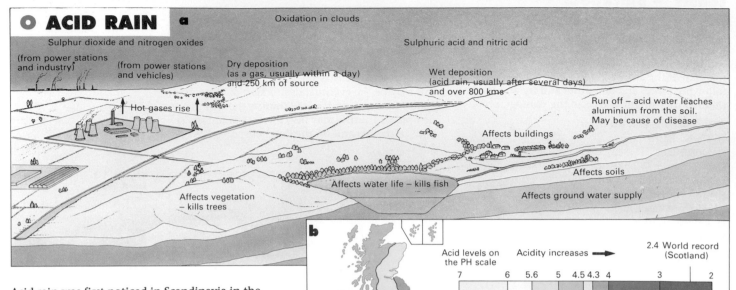

◯ ACID RAIN a

Oxidation in clouds

Sulphur dioxide and nitrogen oxides

Sulphuric acid and nitric acid

(from power stations and industry)

(from power stations and vehicles)

Dry deposition (as a gas, usually within a day) and 250 km of source

Wet deposition (acid rain, usually after several days) and over 800 kms

Hot gases rise

Run off – acid water leaches aluminium from the soil. May be cause of disease

Affects buildings

Affects soils

Affects water life – kills fish

Affects ground water supply

Affects vegetation – kills trees

b

Acid levels on the PH scale

Acidity increases ➡

2.4 World record (Scotland)

| 7 | 6 | 5.6 | 5 | 4.5 | 4.3 | 4 | 3 | 2 |

Neutral distilled water | Clean rain | Acid rain | Fish die | | Apple juice | Vinegar

5.3   5.0   4.5   4.3

Prevailing winds

Figure 14.1
a) Causes and consequences of acid rain

b) Acidity of rainfall in the UK, 1988

Acid rain was first noticed in Scandinavia in the 1950s when large numbers of fresh water fish died. Research showed that the water in which these fish had lived contained more than average amounts of acid. Later it was discovered that this extra acid had been carried by rain, hence the term 'acid rain'. The acid is formed in the air by coal-fired power stations which give our sulphur dioxide and nitrogen oxide (Figure 14.1). These are carried by prevailing winds across seas and national frontiers to be deposited directly on to the earth's surface (dry deposition) or converted into acids (sulphur and nitric acid) which then fall to the ground in the rain (wet deposition). Clean rainwater has a pH value of between 5 and 6 (pH7 is neutral). Today, over much of North-west Europe, the pH readings are between 4 and 4.5 with the lowest ever being 2.4 (Figure 14.2b). A falling pH is the sign of increasing acidity, and remember when pH falls by one unit it means that the level of acid has increased ten times.

The effects of acid rain

These can be summarised as:

■ Increased acidity of lakes where concentrations may kill the fish and plant life.

■ Increased acidity of soils which reduces the number of crops that can be grown.

■ Forests being destroyed as important nutrients (calcium and potassium) are washed away (leached). These are replaced by manganese and aluminium which are harmful to root growth.

■ Water supplies are becoming more acidic and this could become a future health hazard.

■ Buildings are also being eroded by chemical action due to acid rain. St. Paul's Cathedral has lost over 2 cm thickness of stone since it was built.

The power stations in the Midlands and North-west England (Figure 6.3) are considered a major cause of acid rain. Pollutants are carried by the prevailing south-westerly winds and deposited in Eastern Britain and further afield in Scandinavia. Although since 1986 the British Government has increased the money available to combat power station emissions, many people consider that far more needs to be done. This need has become more urgent as it is now widely accepted that power stations and car fumes contribute to the 'Greenhouse Effect'.

The Greenhouse Effect

The Greenhouse Effect is the result of a build up of gases in the atmosphere. These greenhouse gases are made up of:

■ 49% carbon dioxide resulting from the burning, mainly in power stations, of fossil fuels. The burning of the tropical rainforests also releases carbon dioxide and leaves fewer trees to absorb it. It is claimed that the amount of carbon dioxide in the atmosphere has increased by 20% in the last century, and could rise by another 20% by the year 2010.

■ 18% methane released from animal dung, rubbish dumps, farming (e.g. rice in South-east Asia) and cut peat bogs.

■ 14% CFCs (chlorofluorocarbons) from aerosols, foam packaging and refrigerators. These produce the most damaging greenhouse gas.

■ 6% nitrous oxide from car exhausts, power stations and agricultural fertiliser.

■ 13% from 36 known other gases.

The earth is warmed during the day by incoming (solar) radiation from the sun. At night the earth loses this heat by infra-red radiation. If, throughout the world, incoming and outgoing radiation is balanced, then global temperatures will remain the same. However outgoing infra-red radiation can not pass through the greenhouse gases. As these gases increase they act like a blanket trapping the earth's heat and causing a rise in global temperatures. Figure 14.2a shows a rise in world temperature of 0.5°C this century. Estimates suggest a further rise of between 1.5°C and 4.5°C by the end of next century. Although this would make southern England as warm as the present day Costa Brava the warmer temperatures would melt polar ice caps causing a rise in sea-level of between 1 to 5 metres, and the drowning of many low lying areas of Britain (Figure 14.2b) and the world.

■ Seven of this century's warmest ten years globally were in the 1980s.

■ 1989-90 was Britain's warmest winter for over 300 years.

■ British sea levels are rising faster than was predicted at first

○ THE THINNING OZONE LAYER

Ozone is concentrated in a layer 25 to 30 km above sea-level. It acts as a shield, protecting the earth from the damaging effects of ultra-violet radiation from the sun. There is serious concern because this shield appears to be breaking down. Each spring a hole, the size of the USA, appears over Antarctica, (Figure 14.3) while in 1989 a small one was recorded for the first time in the Arctic. As more ultra-violet radiation reaches the earth then the incidence of skin cancer is likely to increase — those with fair skin being at greater risk than people with black skin. Ozone is being destroyed by humans releasing a family of chemicals containing chlorine into the atmosphere — the chlorofluorocarbons or CFCs. The major culprits include aerosols such as hair spray and deodorants, refrigerator coolant and manufacturing processes which include foam packaging. Scientists claim that a 1% depletion in ozone causes a 5% increase in the cases of skin cancer, and that there has been a 3% depletion since 1970. In 1987 40 countries agreed to reduce the use of CFCs by 50% by 1999. In 1989 the EC agreed to try to ban all CFCs by 1997 while in Britain there was an advertising campaign for the sale of 'ozone-friendly products'.

Figure 14.3 The Ozone 'hole' over the Antarctic

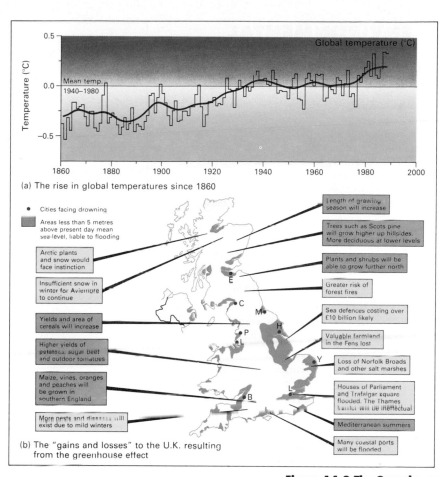

(a) The rise in global temperatures since 1860

- ● Cities facing drowning
- ▦ Areas less than 5 metres above present day mean sea-level, liable to flooding

Arctic plants and snow would face instinction

Insufficient snow in winter for Aviemore to continue

Yields and area of cereals will increase

Higher yields of potatoes, sugar beet and outdoor tomatoes

Maize, vines, oranges and peaches will be grown in southern England

More pests and diseases will exist due to mild winters

Length of growing season will increase

Trees such as Scots pine will grow higher up hillsides. More deciduous at lower levels

Plants and shrubs will be able to grow further north

Greater risk of forest fires

Sea defences costing over £10 billion likely

Valuable farmland in the Fens lost

Loss of Norfolk Broads and other salt marshes

Houses of Parliament and Trafalgar square flooded. The Thames barrier will be ineffectual

Mediterranean summers

Many coastal ports will be flooded

(b) The "gains and losses" to the U.K. resulting from the greenhouse effect

Figure 14.2 The Greenhouse Effect
a) The rise in global temperatures since 1860
b) The 'gains and losses' to the UK resulting from the Greenhouse Effect

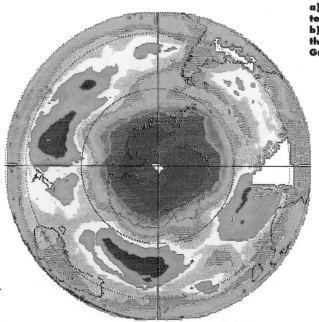

DAY:267   SEP 24, 1987

Low-density   Scale (in Dobson Units)   High-density

125   525

September average ozone concentration over Antarctic

○ ENVIRONMENTAL GAIN OR LOSS

The Sullom Voe oil terminal

The Shetland Islands were an isolated and sparsely populated area until the discovery of North Sea oil. With the building of an oil terminal, it was hoped that the economic gain would not cause the same environmental and social losses that the copper and zinc smelting areas of the Lower Swansea Valley experienced.

Sullom Voe (Figure 14.5) was chosen because of its:

■ Nearness to the North Sea oilfields.

■ Its deep inshore waters leading to the even deeper fiord-type Yell Sound (Figure 14.4).

■ Relative shelter in a gale-prone area.

■ Sparsely populated hinterland.

■ Moraine and peat soils which were easily excavated for the terminal and its associated new power station.

The terminal is a receiving and despatch centre. Oil comes via two pipelines from the Brent and Ninian fields (Figure 6.6). It is here that any gas and water is separated from the oil, after which the oil and gas are taken by tanker to refineries and markets. Even by 1980 this terminal was handling over half of Britain's oil, and this rose to three-quarters by 1985.

The design of the terminal takes the environment into full consideration. Every effort has been made to try to avoid oil spillage, yet if this should occur, a full containment plan can immediately be introduced. While some environmental loss must occur, the oil companies have made efforts not to ruin the natural scenery and wildlife (Figure 14.6).

Below are summarised some of the economic, social and environmental gains and losses of the oil terminal and its effects on the present generation and the consequences for future generations.

Sullom Voe — gains and losses

■ After the construction of the terminal finished, unemployment began to rise again. The 6000 workers at the 1978 peak declined to under 1000 by 1983.

■ New discoveries may be made to the west and north of the mainland thereby increasing employment again.

■ Money gained from oil revenues is helping to re-establish the traditional industries, especially sheep rearing, dairy farming and fishing. A new mill for Shetland wool has also been set up.

■ The heliport is not being fully used as modern planes can bypass it.

Figure 14.4 Location of Sullom Voe, Shetland Islands

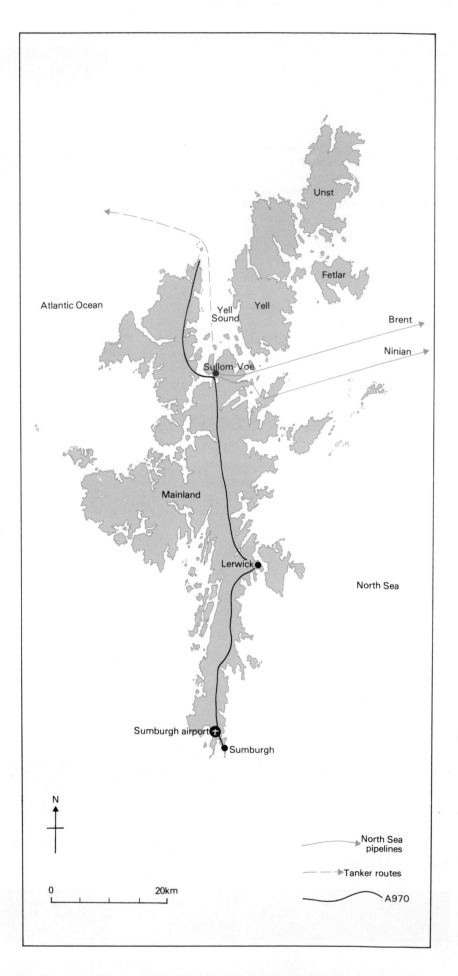

Figure 14.6 Shetland coastline at Mousa showing sparsely populated coastline which provided important wildlife habitats. This was typical of the coastline before oil terminal development

Figure 14.5 Sullom Voe Oil terminal

Sullom Voe — gains and losses

Before 1975	1980s	
Population: 17 000	Population: 23 000	*Economic gain*
Small airport with a few annual passengers (at Sumburgh)	Enlarged modernised airport with Heliport. Passenger trade increased ten times.	*Economic gain*
Limited job opportunities and limited income	i) 6000 extra jobs at the terminal at peak ii) Much higher salaries iii) Income from 'disturbance money' and harbour dues	*Economic gain*
Traditional industries of crofting, knitwear, fishing	Fishing declined, knitwear 50% reduced, decline in crofting. Some reversal to cottage industries.	*Economic loss*
Limited social amenities	Improved social amenities (schools, shops, health)	*Social gain*
Rural depopulation, especially teenagers to mainland	Reversal as better jobs now locally	*Economic gain*
Small close knit community	Influx of many newcomers changing society	*Social loss*
No help to national economy	Oil of major importance to British Oil. By 1985 50% of the UK's oil was from Brentfield.	*Economic gain*
Unspoilt, attractive scenery to the north though of relatively poor grazing land	i) Visual unattractiveness of oil terminal ii) Noise iii) Air pollution iv) Threats of explosions and oil spillage	*Environmental loss*
Breeding ground for over one million seabirds. Other wildlife untouched	i) Many seabirds killed by oil spillage in 1978 ii) Threat of future disasters due to storms and fog — port is already closed 50 days a year due to bad weather	*Environmental loss*
Little disease	More infectious diseases	*Social loss*

⚪ HAZARDOUS WASTES

Hazardous wastes include toxic, ignitable, corrosive, explosive, oily, irritant and dangerously active materials. A major environmental and health problem is how to store, or safely dispose of, these wastes. The wastes include arsenic, mercury, paint sludge, detergents, residues from the metal plating industry (the Lower Swansea Valley in the 19th century), micro-chip degreasing agents (from modern hi-tech industries) and especially those from the nuclear industry. The leaking of these wastes has been linked with various cancers, birth defects and miscarriages, brain damage, and blood and nervous disorders.

Three present day methods used in Britain are:

1 Sealing waste in drums which have then to be safely stored. However drums are not always labelled and may, at a later stage, explode or corrode spilling out their contents, e.g. unlabelled drums washed ashore at Brighton in February 1990, and found to contain lethal poisons.
2 Using landfill sites which provide a short term economic advantage but may create longer term environmental problems if materials slowly leach through the rubbish into the soil, rivers or underground water supplies.
3 By the incineration of rubbish. This may, if not processed correctly, result in the release of toxic gases into the atmosphere and have serious effects on wild life.

Britain is believed to be a net receiver of hazardous wastes as its controls on disposal are less strict than in other countries.

Nuclear wastes

There are at present four sources of radioactive waste in Britain. Most waste results from the production of nuclear energy for electricity. The remainder comes from the production of nuclear weapons, medical use and research, and industries using radioisotopes. A future fifth source may come from the dismantling of old nuclear power stations and nuclear submarines. Every radioactive substance has a 'half-life'. This is the length of time needed for half its initial radioactivity to die away. Iodine, with a half-life of eight days, becomes 'safe' relatively quickly. In contrast, plutonium 239, produced by nuclear reactors, has a half-life of 250 000 years (it is still lethal after half a million years) and uranium 238 a half-life of 2.4 million years.

Radioactive waste, as shown in Figure 14.7, can be divided into three types based upon the level of radioactivity and the half-life. The reprocessing of nuclear waste, mainly done at Sellafield in Cumbria, is highly controversial. Opponents claim the industry is dangerous and unsafe, is responsible for high rates of leukemia in local children and has polluted the Irish Sea killing marine life and making Cumbrian beaches unsafe. Supporters argue that the industry provides 40 000 jobs nationally, either directly or indirectly, is the major employer of labour in an area of Cumbria with traditionally high unemployment, brings much needed wealth into the UK, and does not contribute to the Greenhouse Effect or acid rain.

Figure 14.8 A hazardous waste transporter

Figure 14.7 Storage of nuclear wastes

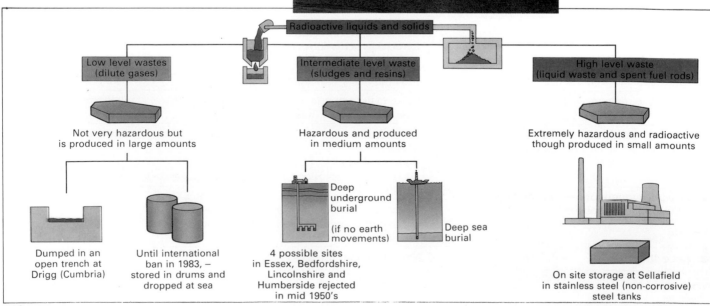

Radioactive liquids and solids

Low level wastes (dilute gases)	Intermediate level waste (sludges and resins)	High level waste (liquid waste and spent fuel rods)
Not very hazardous but is produced in large amounts	Hazardous and produced in medium amounts	Extremely hazardous and radioactive though produced in small amounts
Dumped in an open trench at Drigg (Cumbria) Until international ban in 1983, – stored in drums and dropped at sea	Deep underground burial (if no earth movements) Deep sea burial 4 possible sites in Essex, Bedfordshire, Lincolnshire and Humberside rejected in mid 1950's	On site storage at Sellafield in stainless steel (non-corrosive) steel tanks

Canvey Island (Essex)

Study Figure 14.9 below, which is a map of Canvey Island, then explain why you think that this area has attracted so many industries and why the inhabitants of Canvey Island fear for their health and lives.

Now study and complete Figure 14.10 which requires you to use own judgement on the question of the quality of life for you and future generations. There is no right or wrong answer, but it may help you to make a value judgement for the future.

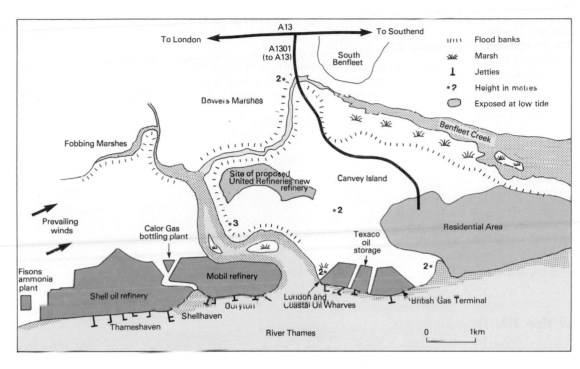

Figure 14.9 Canvey Island, Essex showing location of major oil refineries and gas terminals

Figure 14.10 Quality of life matrix

Proposals affecting quality of life	Rank order of value to people today 1 = most value 12 = least value	Rank order of loss to environment 1 = least loss 12 = greatest loss	Rank order of spoiling the environment for future generations 1 = least damage 12 = greatest damage
Building a new reservoir in a national park			
Building a nuclear power station on a river estuary			
Building an urban motorway from a major motorway towards a city centre			
Demolishing old inner-city houses for a ring road			
Re-opening a quarry in an area of outstanding beauty yet with much unemployment			
Building a hypermarket on an edge of city greenfield site			
Building a new oil refinery on a Scottish island			
Building a new undercover pedestrianised CBD shopping centre			
Building London's third airport			
Building a large holiday camp next to a small village with many elderly residents			
Providing modernisation grants for old inner-city houses			
Enlarging a small village near to a large city			

◯ HIGHLAND DEVELOPMENT

The Highlands and Islands Development Board (HIDB)

The North-west of Scotland underwent a rapid decline in population in the years preceding 1975 (Figure 15.1). Those people who remained in this area found it increasingly more difficult to make a living from farming (crofting), fishing, and tweed manufacture. As a result the Highlands and Islands Development Board (HIDB) was set up by Act of Parliament in 1965. This Board is responsible to the Secretary of State for Scotland, and has two main functions:

- To assist the people of the Highlands and Islands to improve their economic and social conditions.
- To enable the Highlands and Islands to play a more effective part in the economic and social development of the nation.

The location of the areas within the HIDB are shown in Figure 15.2.

The achievements of the HIDB

A further measure of the Board's success, aided by the discovery and exploitation of North Sea oil, can be seen in the reversal of population change within the HIDB area (Figure 15.3). The HIDB has been involved in the following areas:

Tourism

Tourism has been aided by considerable investment. Such areas as the Spey Valley (Aviemore), for example, have numerous HIDB

hotels and self-catering holiday facilities. Other projects include a comprehensive network of tourist information centres, the extension of the tourist season, and the increased provision of amenities in more remote, yet equally attractive, areas.

Industry

The HIDB help in the development of small to medium sized manufacturing industries (Figure 15.4) by encouraging existing firms as well as

Figure 15.2 HIDB areas

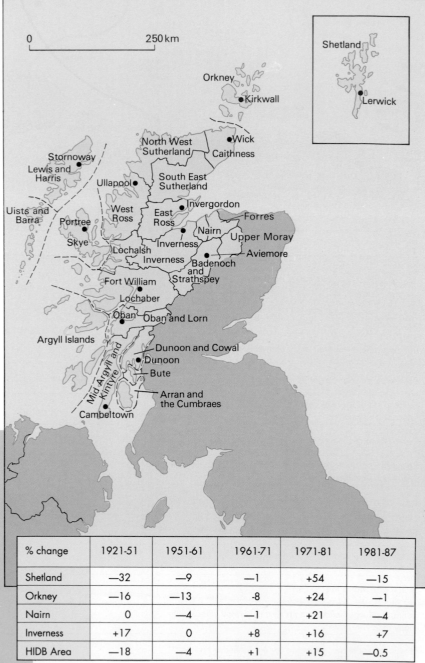

Figure 15.1 Population of the Highlands and Islands Development Board area

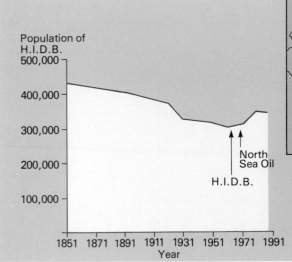

% change	1921-51	1951-61	1961-71	1971-81	1981-87
Shetland	−32	−9	−1	+54	−15
Orkney	−16	−13	-8	+24	−1
Nairn	0	−4	−1	+21	−4
Inverness	+17	0	+8	+16	+7
HIDB Area	−18	−4	+1	+15	−0.5

Figure 15.3 Population changes within the HIDB areas

assisting new companies. In the more remote Orkneys and Outer Hebrides, community co-operatives have been developed to provide work and to unify local populations. The Board also provide 'advanced factories' on industrial estates but it needs many small firms to offset even one large scale closure such as the paper mill at Corpach, the aluminium smelter at Invergordon and the oil platform fabrication yard at Nigg. Industries which have developed include pine furniture, Caithness Glass, ski-making, saw mills, leather goods, electronics and Harris Tweed. Alness and Invergordon have become an Enterprise Zone (page 124).

Farming

Crofting (Figure 15.5) remains the major type of farming but whereas those employed in farming are still declining in numbers, output has increased. The HIDB have been able to offer up to 50% grants for new developments, as well as advice on accounting, transport and marketing, and help in the form of interest relief grants. In 1981, 900 of the 18 000 crofts still provided full-time work for those in farming, while the remainder were working as part-time farmers.

Grants have also enabled the setting up of a deer farm (Figure 15.7) and the increase of cattle on many farms.

Fishing

The HIDB have made considerable investment in new boats, the Breasclete fish drying factory (Lewis), and fish farms (both salt and fresh water) of which there were 68 by 1987. Fishing is especially important as each job at sea provides two jobs on shore.

Transport

The Board is chief adviser to the Secretary of State for Scotland on Transport in the area, and is pressing for an integrated system including all forms of freight and passenger transport. A major concern is the increasing costs of transport in a generally rural, remote region. Roll on/roll off ferries operate to most islands.

Figure 15.4 The former railway station at Strathpeffer, Ross and Cromarty now provides an attractive location for craft workshops

Social and cultural

The Board also supports schemes which improve local community assets such as village halls, museums and regional arts. A showpiece is the Eden Court Theatre in Inverness where the headquarters of the HIDB are based.

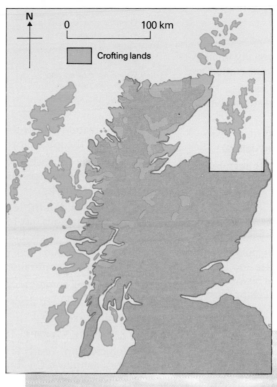

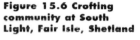

Figure 15.5 Crofting lands

Figure 15.6 Crofting community at South Light, Fair Isle, Shetland

Figure 15.7 Deer farming, West Yorkshire

○ GOVERNMENT AID

Farming subsidies, road and rail development, the development of present and future energy supplies, new towns, planning permission for new industries, and special grants for areas of high unemployment are all examples of government intervention. A government may intervene for the following reasons:

■ To gain votes.

■ To prevent social unrest, especially in areas where unemployment and immigration are high.

■ To prevent the breakdown in the quality of life of an area.

■ To further economic progress in order to capitalise on land, labour and capital.

■ To encourage growth in certain regions and to control it in others with a view to levelling out regional disparities.

How a government can help

Successive governments have encouraged industry to move to assisted areas. The size and location of these have changed with time. The most recent are shown in Figure 15.8. The classification of these areas and what provisions are made for each one, are given in Figure 15.9.

Aid to these areas includes:

■ Industrial development certificates which control where a firm can locate. These were first issued by the British government in 1947.

Figure 15.8 Assisted Areas since November 1984

	STANDARD AREA	INTERMEDIATE AREA	DEVELOPMENT AREA	SPECIAL DEVELOPMENT AREA N.IRELAND
Government built factories	Not available	Available at low rents and rates, possibly up to two years rent free		Similar, but possibly free, for up to five years
Factory building	None	25% to 35%	Possibly 35% but up to 45%	35% to 45%
Government loans available	No	No	Yes	Yes
Grant to clear derelict land	50%	75%	85%	85%
Training grants	No	£10 per week, with smaller grants for women		
Other grants for training Centres	No	Yes	Yes	Yes
Grants for moving and housing key workers	No	Yes	Yes	Yes
Subsidy of fuel costs	None	None	None	6%—12%

Figure 15.9 Classification of Assisted Areas

■ The creation of new towns in order to take work to the unemployed.

■ Providing advanced factories' and industrial estates with services already provided (e.g. roads, electricity).

■ Financial aid in the form of removal grants, rent free periods, tax relief on new machinery, and reduced interest rates (Figure 15.9.)

■ New government offices (Figure 15.10) in an attempt to decentralise.

■ Improving communications and accessibility.

■ subsidies to keep firms going which otherwise would close down.

■ Retraining schemes.

■ Job creation, Youth Training Schemes (YTS) and Manpower Creation Schemes (MCS).

■ Creation of special development areas and enterprise zones (page 124).

■ EC funds following industrial closures (e.g. steelworks).

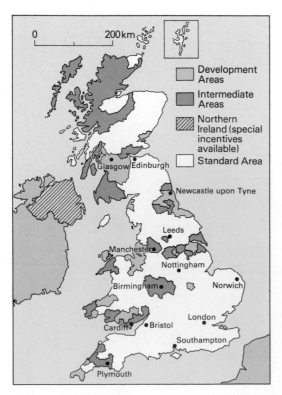

Figure 15.8 Assisted Areas since November 1984

0 — 200km

- Development Areas
- Intermediate Areas
- Northern Ireland (special incentives available)
- Standard Area

Glasgow · Edinburgh
Newcastle upon Tyne
Leeds
Manchester
Nottingham
Birmingham · Norwich
London
Cardiff · Bristol
Southampton
Plymouth

Cumbernauld (National Savings)
Newcastle upon Tyne (Ministry of Pensions and National Insurance)
Durham (National Savings)
St. Annes (Ernie)
Bootle (Giro)
Llantrisant (Royal Mint)
Basingstoke (Civil Service)
Southend (V.A.T. Computer Centre)
Swansea (Car Licences)
Southampton (Ordnance Survey)
Titchfield (Population Census)

Figure 15.10 Location of major British Government Departments

Aid in Northern Ireland

Northern Ireland's industrial structure has changed dramatically since 1950. This structural decline has taken place in the three traditional industries of:

- Agriculture — provided jobs for 10% of the workforce in 1950, but only 1.8% in 1985.

- Shipbuilding — Harland and Wolff who employed 24 500 in 1950, only employed 5200 in 1985.

- Textiles — the 65 000 employed in this industry in 1950 had fallen to 14 000 in 1985.

Together with an expanding population (one of the highest birth rates in Europe), government policy has been geared to creating new types of jobs. As Figure 15.8 shows, Northern Ireland is a special development area, and the various incentives listed in Figure 15.9 have attracted many multinational companies whose parent firm is located in either North America or the EC countries (Figure 15.12).

By 1982 44% of manufacturing employment was in government-assisted projects such as car components, synthetic fibres, electrical and electronic goods, clothing, knitwear, rubber and plastic products. Many of these foreign based firms were located in Northern Ireland to gain a tariff free entry into the EC. Figure 15.11 shows that most USA based firms have become located in Belfast and the New Town of Craigavon, whilst most British and European companies have built their factories in smaller provincial towns. However, such companies make little impact on unemployment (compared with 20 000 job losses at ICI and Courtaulds in 1980). Yet these new companies do try to attract equal numbers of Protestant and Roman Catholic workers. This is not easy, as traditionally it has been the Protestants who have provided the skilled labour. Investment has not only come from the British Government. EC funds are also being used to modernise Aldergrove airport and to help to build the Skyvan (the Short Brothers' latest aeroplane), as well as to assist farming. The EC lists Northern Ireland as one of its five least prosperous regions, and has launched an operation to try to restore economic and social structures within Belfast. In 1981, parts of Belfast were made into an enterprise zone by the British Government (Figure 15.13).

During 1984, Northern Ireland received £5m from the EC for improvements to Belfast Airport's subsidiary operational runway, improvements to both rail and road networks, additional facilities at Belfast Harbour and the Port of Londonderry, provision of a wet-weather recreation complex at Irvinestone (Co. Fermanagh) and an extension of the promenade at Newcastle (Co. Down).

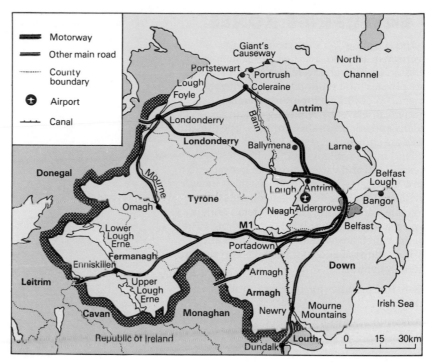

Figure 15.11 Northern Ireland — towns and communications

Figure 15.12 Multinational companies in Northern Ireland

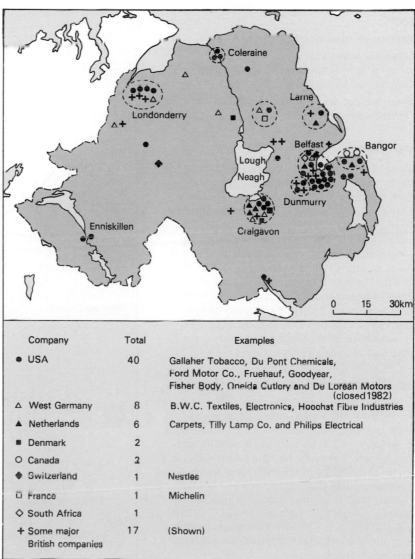

Company	Total	Examples
● USA	40	Gallaher Tobacco, Du Pont Chemicals, Ford Motor Co., Fruehauf, Goodyear, Fisher Body, Oneida Cutlery and De Lorean Motors (closed 1982)
△ West Germany	8	B.W.C. Textiles, Electronics, Hoechst Fibre Industries
▲ Netherlands	6	Carpets, Tilly Lamp Co. and Philips Electrical
■ Denmark	2	
○ Canada	2	
◆ Switzerland	1	Nestles
▢ France	1	Michelin
◇ South Africa	1	
+ Some major British companies	17	(Shown)

○ ENTERPRISE ZONES

Enterprise zones (EZs) were created by the Government in 1980. The first EZs came into operation in 1981 and were planned for areas in acute physical and economic decay, with the aim of creating conditions for industrial and commercial revival by removing certain tax burdens and administrative controls. The present 26 EZs are shown in Figure 15.13. All sites have had land made available to them for development, and vary in size from between 50 to over 400 hectares. Proposals for EZs must include provision for light industry, general industry, wholesale warehousing and small retail outlets. (Hypermarkets are considered to be too big.) The benefits which are available to both new and existing industrial and commercial enterprises in the zones include:

- Rate free premises for 10 years (until August 1991).

- Maximum grants for machinery and buildings.

- Applications from firms wishing to locate in EZs are given top priority.

- Employers are exempt from industrial training levies.

- Exemption from development land tax.

- 100% allowances are given for the construction, extension, or improvement of commercial and industrial premises.

- No industrial development certificates are needed.

Clydebank

Clydebank (population 54 000) was selected in the 1970s by the Scottish Development Agency (SDA) to form a task force whose job it was: 'To look at industrial renewal, and to attempt environmental planning in areas of industrial waste land.' The task force was given a site on an old steelworks, and was funded by both the Strathclyde Regional Council and the Clydebank District Council. Yet even with the 50% rate reduction, it proved difficult to attract new firms. Then in 1979 the large Singer Sewing Machine Company closed with a loss of a further 3000 jobs, and the SDA were authorised by the Government to buy the 35 hectare vacant site.

The Clydebank enterprise zone

As a result of the British Government's policy to create in 1981 11 enterprise zones, Clydebank with its task force, was chosen. In all, 240 hectares were set aside — 200 hectares in Clydebank and 40 in Glasgow (Figure 15.14). The EZ included seven industrial sites, but not the John Brown Engineering works (2000 workforce and famous for having built the Queen Elizabeth and Mary liners and making gas turbines) nor the UIE (750 workforce) which is a French consortium making oil rigs and also operates in parts of the old John Brown yards (Figure 15.16).

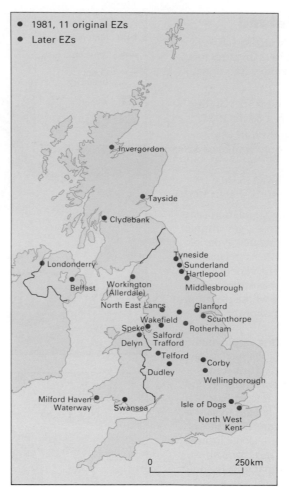

- 1981, 11 original EZs
- Later EZs

Figure 15.13 Enterprise Zones

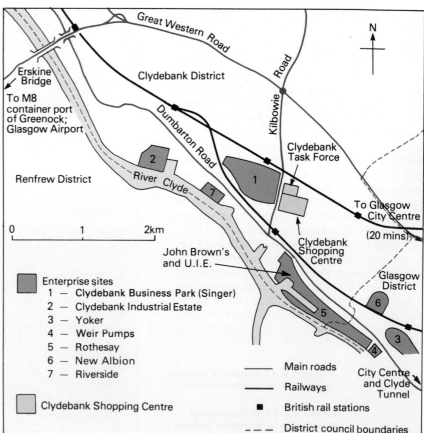

Figure 15.14 Clydebank, Glasgow

Enterprise sites
1 — Clydebank Business Park (Singer)
2 — Clydebank Industrial Estate
3 — Yoker
4 — Weir Pumps
5 — Rothesay
6 — New Albion
7 — Riverside

Clydebank Shopping Centre

Main roads
Railways
British rail stations
District council boundaries

The Clydebank Business Park

Here the SDA have demolished or refurbished the former Singer works, creating a new town atmosphere near a town centre. This area is shown in Figure 15.15 in the middle to the right. The advantages of this site include:

- Access by road to Glasgow city centre which takes 15 minutes.
- 8 km from Glasgow airport, and 23 km from the container port at Greenock via Erskine Bridge.
- There are 12 electric trains per hour to Glasgow and it takes only 25 minutes to a rail freight terminal. The site has its own railway station.
- It is 5 km from the M8 and the national motorway system.
- The drive to Glasgow airport takes 12 minutes.
- A workforce of ½ million, many highly skilled, live within 30 minutes travelling time of the site.
- The Clydebank task force are there to help new industries.
- Advanced and purpose built factories.
- The site is adjacent to Clydebank's new shopping centre and close to the new Scottish exhibition centre.
- The attractive scenery of Loch Lomond and the Kilpatrick Hills are only 20 minutes away.

Clydebank is generally recognised as the most successful of the original 11 EZs. Within three years (September 1984) it attracted 260 companies, provided 200 000 m² of industrial accommodation in a landscaped environment, and created 2932 jobs (remember, in their heyday, John Brown had employed 10 000 and Singer 18 000). Clydebank Business Park (the former Singer factory, Figure 15.15) now houses Radio Clyde; a 10 000 m² office development founded by the National Westminster Bank and one three times larger developed by Wykeland Ltd (Humberside); a refurbished office building occupied by Semicomplex; a series of small business units and with plans for a 60 bedroom hotel, and a multi-million pound sports and leisure complex. Certainly the town has a wider industrial base than in previous years.

Clydebank International Trade Zone

Within the International Trade Zone, companies involved in import and export have access to the duty relief facilities of a European Community duty-free zone. Given customs approval, no duty need be paid on any goods brought into the Zone, manufactured or assembled, and subsequently exported outside the European Community.

Figure 15.15 1981. Central Clydebank looking west with the first phase of the new shopping centre in the foreground and the largely cleared site of the old Singer factory behind. In the distance can be seen the Erskine Bridge over the River Clyde, with the container port of Greenock beyond.

Figure 15.16 Aerial view showing the John Brown Engineering works and UIE extending along the river front. Clydebank lies to the right of the river and Renfrew to the left. The old Singer works is in the middle right distance, and the Kilpatrick Hills behind.

SOLIHULL S.F.C. LIBRARY

● AN ABUSED RESOURCE

Sources and consequences of sea pollution

Sources

■ **Rivers** Rivers which discharge into British seas are the major source of dangerous chemicals. Nitrates and phosphates originate as fertiliser., pesticides and herbicides, also spread by farmers, are very slow to break down. Some EC rivers discharge raw sewage.

Industry discharges waste into rivers which, in time, pollute estuaries and coastal waters. Some of the most toxic chemicals are the chlorinated hydrocarbons (HHCs) which include Lindane and DDT.

■ **Direct discharge** Pipelines are responsible for large amounts of untreated sewage being discharged into the sea — 85% within 100 m of the low water mark.

Nuclear installations, such as the reprocessing plant at Sellafield, release low level radioactive material into the sea.

■ **Direct dumping** Sewage sludge which is highly toxic, remains after the treatment of domestic sewage and industrial waste. Most estuaries around Britain — the Thames, Tyne, Humber and Tees — are used as dumping grounds. Industrial effluent includes mercury, cadmium and lead. Coal sludge (Durham) and by-products from the china clay industry (Cornwall) are deposited on beaches. Oil-tankers may illegally wash their decks while at sea.

■ **Incineration** Some of the most hazardous of toxic waste is burnt on two ships based off the coast at Scarborough. Although due to be phased out, this is the only area in the world where incineration is done at sea.

■ **From the atmosphere** Over twice the amount of mercury and seven times the quantity of lead (mainly from car exhausts) enters the North Sea from the air than by rivers.

■ **Accidents** These include wrecks of oil-tankers (Torrey Canyon in 1967 and ships carrying dangerous chemicals (the Perentis which sank in the English Channel in 1989 was carrying Lindane). The blow out of the Bravo Rig in 1977 produced an oil slick 16 km long and 3 km wide in the North Sea. Low level radio-active waste leaks have occurred several times at Sellafield.

Consequences

■ Nitrates over-enrich water causing the growth of algae and a depletion of oxygen. Pesticides and herbicides become concentrated in marine food chains (page 28). Wildlife in estuaries is reduced. Mercury affects the nervous system, Cadmium can cause cancer and lead poisoning results in kidney and brain damage. Many HHCs cause cancer and genetic mutations as they accumulate in the tissues of plants and animals. Lindane may have killed the dolphins in Cardigan Bay (Wales).

■ Tides and currents return much of this sewage to the shore. Many of Britain's 690 major beaches are polluted in this way. This can cause hepatitis and meningitis. Beaches are contaminated and marine life, especially in the Irish Sea, is affected.

■ Breaks down the marine ecosystem (page 28 and Figure 16.2). Affects fish breeding grounds and may kill off those species living on the sea-bed.

■ Creates visual pollution as well as killing wildlife.

■ Kills bird and fish life. Deformed fish have been recognised in areas off the Forth, Humber and Thames estuaries.

■ Creates fumes and smells. The complete destruction of these wastes is impossible.

■ (See rivers above).

■ Major environmental damage. Sea birds and beaches become covered in oil. Interruptions in the marine ecosystem may take years — if ever — to overcome. Supplies of fish may be reduced causing job losses in that industry. Seaweeds die. Chemical dispersants used to clear the oil are equally damaging to fish.

Figure 16.1 Pollution at sea
a) discharge,
b) oil slick at sea,
c) beach pollution,
d) incinerator ship

The marine ecosystem

All parts of any ecosystem link together in the food chain (Figure 16.2). Algae and plankton form the beginning of the marine food chain. There are two types of plankton:

1 phytoplankton is plant matter sustained by sunlight and feeding on nutrients in the water,
2 zooplankton is animal matter which feeds on phytoplankton and on each other.

Fish form the intermediate stage of the chain feeding on plankton, crustaceans or on other fish (which will have previously eaten plankton).

Mammals (dolphins and humans) and birds are at the end of the food chain as they consume the fish.

If any stage in the food chain is affected by pollution the effects are then passed on to succeeding stages in that chain.

Britain's beaches

Britain's beaches, like its seas, are far from clean. In 1975 the EC set limits for pollution of water where people bathed. Beaches were given ten years to reach these basic requirements — the majority of those in Britain failed. The Water Authorities of England and Wales (Figure 5.5) have also been responsible for controlling sewage released into the sea. They have put this low in their order of priorities. Recently they have opened several much longer (2 km) sewage outfalls. Theoretically the sun and sea and disperse sewage naturally, but six months after a new outfall was opened at Southend the sea remained as dirty as before. Water Authorities claim our seas are getting cleaner. The EC, which measures viruses in the water as against our measuring bacteria, are not convinced. It is the viruses which are responsible for hepatitis, meningitis and polio.

Blue Flag beaches and ports

The European Blue Flag Campaign was launched in 1987 with the first awards made in 1988. The Blue Flag for beaches is awarded for high standards of water quality, the absence of untreated sewage outfall, the cleanliness of the beach itself, the presence of safety equipment and the provision of environmental information for the public. A similar award is given to leisure ports and marinas. In 1988 awards were made to 391 beaches and 102 leisure ports/marinas in the EC. Of these only 17 beaches and three ports were in the UK (Figure 16.3). In 1988 Britain introduced a by-law banning dogs on beaches during the summer season. The judges were impressed by the considerable improvements in standard made by several local authorities as public awareness in beach cleanliness was raised — but we have no reason to be complacent!

Figure 16.3 British beaches 1988

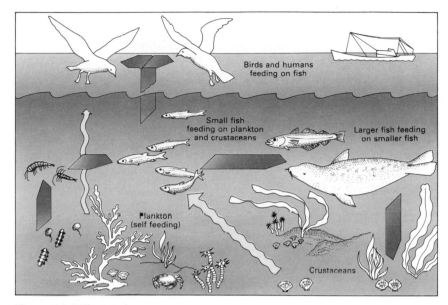

Figure 16.2 The marine ecosystem

Blue flag beaches 1988
▲ Blue flag ports 1988
Coasts of outstanding natural beauty
Urban and industrial areas

BLUE FLAG BEACHES
1 Porthmeor (St. Ives), Cornwall
2 Crinnis (Carlyon Bay), Cornwall
3 Blackpool Sands, Devon
4 Oddiscombe, Torbay
5 Anstey's Cove (or Redgate), Torbay
6 Broadsands, Torbay
7 Corbyn (or Ter Abbey), Torbay
8 Meadfoot, Torbay
9 Paignton, Torbay
10 Exmouth, Devon
11 Sidemouth, Devon
12 Weymouth, Dorset
13 Poole, Dorset
14 Bournemouth
15 Lee-on-Solent, Hampshire
16 Stokes Bay, Hampshire
17 Pembery (or Cefn Sidan), Wales

BLUE FLAG PORTS
1 Westfield Marina, Milford-Haven
2 Swansea Marina
3 Braid Marina, Amble

INDEX